IN SEARCH OF THE LATER HAHNEMANN

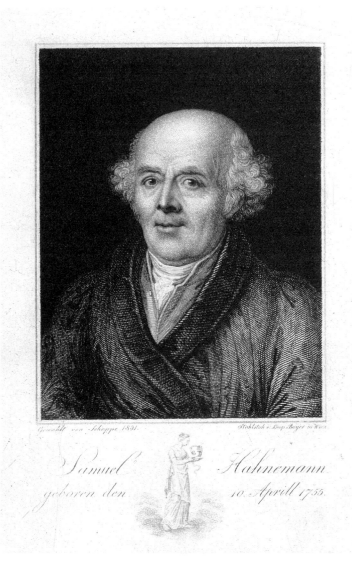

Gemahlt von Schoppe 1831.   Stahlstich v. Leop.Beyer in Wien

Samuel   *Hahnemann*
geboren den   *10. Aprill 1755.*

A steel engraving reproduced by kind permission
of Mr Francis Treuherz, FSHom

In Search of the Later Hahnemann

Rima Handley
DPhil, FSHom

BEACONSFIELD PUBLISHERS LTD
Beaconsfield, Bucks, UK

First published 1997

Archive material supplied and reproduced by kind permission of the Institut für Geschichte der Medizin der Robert Bosch Stiftung, Stuttgart, Germany.

British Library Cataloguing in Publication Data
Handley, Rima
   In Search of the Later Hahnemann. –
   (Beaconsfield Homoeopathic Library; No. 16)
   I. Title   II. Series
   615.532
ISBN 0–906584–35–3

Other Books by Rima Handley

A Homeopathic Love Story, North Atlantic Books, Berkeley, California
Homeopathy for Woman, Thorsons, London
Homeopathy for Emotional Health, Thorsons, London

Phototypeset by Gem Graphics, Trenance, Mawgan Porth, Cornwall in 10 on 12 point Times.
Printed and bound in Great Britain by The Bath Press, Bath

Acknowledgements

This book has been a long time in the writing, and its publication was further delayed by the sudden death of my brother as I approached its closing stages. I should like to thank all those who have encouraged me to keep going with it, especially during that difficult period when completing it seemed to be of the utmost unimportance.

I would like to record my indebtedness to a number of people who have helped while I was working on it. The successive librarians and their staff at the Robert Bosch Institute for the History of Medicine in Stuttgart were particularly helpful: not only did they first introduce me to the material but in a most friendly way allowed me to study it at odd hours, enabling me to make the fullest use of my limited time in Germany. They also provided me with microfiches and unlimited photocopying facilities so that I could continue to study the manuscripts at home.

My receptionist Connie Driver has always been willing to take administrative jobs from me in order to make it possible for me to take more time to write. At the outset of the project the Society of Homoeopaths raised a sum of money to help me to take time off from work to press ahead with the necessary research. Harris and Catherine Coulter also gave me practical help. My colleagues and students at the Northern College of Homeopathic Medicine have read parts of the manuscript at various times, and were always ready to help on queries of style and translation. I am particularly grateful to Nan Beecher-Moore, Chris Conyers, Diana Clarke, Caroline Melody, Glynis Ingram, Gabriela Rieberer, Francis Treuherz and Jude Watson. Glynis Ingram and Nan Beecher-Moore, as always, have supported me in more ways than they would probably recognise. Catherine Coulter and Jacques Baur each read the book critically at an advanced stage and made many valuable suggestions, which I was able to take into account when preparing the final version. I should like to thank them both for their careful and considerate contribution. My publisher John Churchill has been endlessly helpful and supportive.

This book brings to light some material unearthed by Richard Haehl towards the end of his life, but too late for him to publish. I am glad to be able to do something towards continuing the work that he undertook so bravely, many years ago.

Despite all this help, and my own best efforts, there are bound to be mistakes in a book of this nature. These are mine and I look forward to others correcting them. I was once a medievalist, and I used to look with incredulity at the mistakes made by early textual scholars in transcribing and interpreting the texts they worked on, mistakes which seemed so obvious to me following after them. I know that the same will happen with this book – what was obscure to me will be clear to those coming after. However, it has been exciting to have been at the coal face when the mine was opened up; I hope that others will be able to undertake finer work once the tunnels have been excavated!

R.H.

Contents

Introduction

All homeopaths are familiar with the story of Samuel Hahnemann's early life, its trials and vicissitudes, his piece-by-piece formulation of the principles of homeopathy and their painstaking verification in practice, as well as with the story of his success and failure in Leipzig followed by his self-chosen exile to Köthen in 1821.

We are not, however, so familiar with the story of his later years, the years in which, having married a rich young French wife, the Marquise Melanie d'Hervilly, he moved to Paris, and, at the age of eighty, once again set up a successful homeopathic practice, publicising homeopathy from the capital of the fashionable world in a way he could never have done from the small Saxon town where he had been living for the previous fourteen years.

It was in Paris that Hahnemann achieved his greatest renown and where he was, at last, honoured as he always should have been for his remarkable achievements. It was in Paris that he completed the second edition of his *Chronic Diseases* and his final revision of the *Organon*. It was in Paris that he put into practical effect the implications of his theory of chronic disease, the miasm theory, as it has come to be known. It was in Paris that he experimented with high potencies and pushed his conception of the infinitesimal dose to undreamed-of lengths in developing the LM potency.

This book is the story of Hahnemann's practice of homeopathy during the last years of his life in Paris, a period hitherto little studied and much misunderstood. The story is based for the first time on Hahnemann's actual casebooks, up till now left substantially unexamined in a German library. These reveal a rather different Samuel Hahnemann from the apparently confident master with whom we have become familiar through the pages of his published works.

We see here the private experimentation which underpinned the assurance of his public utterances. We see him literally 'practising' homeopathy, obliged to try numerous different methods of prescribing

1

with his complex Parisian patients, guided not by any dogma but by the spirit of enquiry which had always informed his own learning.

These last casebooks show how Hahnemann adopted a new method of prescribing in the wake of his discovery of the psoric miasm. He no longer prescribed solely on the 'totality of symptoms' he had advocated for so long, but often prescribed miasmatically, usually clearing the psoric miasm at the outset of a case, before proceeding with any more individual prescribing.

He also prescribed in the higher potencies, about which he had first written in a note to the fifth edition of the *Organon* (paragraph 287), changing his methods to accommodate them, prescribing in liquid doses frequently repeated, abandoning the familiar practice of giving one dose and waiting for its action to cease before considering any repetition.

We see him tentatively moving towards what he considered to be his ultimate achievement in releasing spirit from matter: his discovery of the LM potency.

We see him making successful cures, of course, but we also see him making mistakes, improvising, getting stuck and lost in his cases. We see him trying different ways of coping with the responses to remedies, especially with aggravations.

We see him developing his materia medica from the fifty or so remedies which he had at the beginning of his practice to the nearly two hundred which he had by the end of his life. We see him prescribing new and unusual remedies, nosodes, poorly proved and even unproved substances, in his attempts to wrest his patients from the jaws of disease.

Above all we see him experimental, tentative, enquiring, trusting the process he had himself formulated, trusting that if symptoms were indeed the only expression of disease, then removal of the symptoms must result in removal of the disease. If the remedy chosen did not remove the symptoms, then he chose another remedy. If the symptoms aggravated, he often saw the aggravation as an indication for another remedy. If the symptoms disappeared he often put a double exclamation mark in the margin. It seems that surprise at the fact that homeopathy works is something that never leaves even the best prescribers!

We see here the real Hahnemann, Hahnemann at his everyday work. As the existential psychotherapist Irvin Yalom has written:

'In their everyday work, therapists, if they are to relate to their patients in an authentic fashion, experience considerable uncertainty ... The capacity to tolerate uncertainty is a prerequisite for the profession. Though the public may believe that therapists guide patients systematically and sure-handedly through predictable stages of therapy to a foreknown goal, such is rarely the case: instead, therapists frequently wobble, improvise, and grope for direction. The powerful temptation to achieve certainty through embracing an ideological school and a tight therapeutic system is treacherous: such belief may block the uncertain and spontaneous encounter necessary for effective therapy.'*

To read Hahnemann's cases is to see him 'wobble, improvise and grope for direction' a great deal. It is to see him as a whole person and to share in the process of the making of homeopathy.

R.H.

*Yalom, I. D., *Love's Executioner and Other Tales of Psychotherapy*, Bloomsbury, London 1989.

Chapter 1

The Context

Samuel Hahnemann was born in 1755 in Meissen in Saxony: he died in Paris in 1843. The basic details of his early life, though few, are well known.[1] After a youth fraught with difficulties (arising from the impoverishment of his middle-class family in Frederick the Great's Seven Years War), he eventually trained as a doctor, studying in Leipzig and Vienna before finally qualifying at Erlangen in 1779. At the age of 27 he married Johanna Henriette Küchler, the daughter of an apothecary, and for the first few years of his married life he managed to earn some kind of living by combining medical practice and the translation of medical and scientific texts. He worked as a doctor in the face of his own increasing dissatisfaction with current medical practice, salving his conscience by treating patients as far as possible only with diet and exercise, using a minimum of drugs. In 1790, however, he gave up his practice, saying that he could no longer bring himself to follow such a murderous trade:

'My sense of duty would not easily allow me to treat the unknown pathological state of my suffering brethren with these unknown medicines. The thought of becoming in this way a murderer or a malefactor towards the life of my fellow human beings was most terrible to me, so terrible and disturbing that I wholly gave up my practice in the first years of my married life . . . and occupied myself solely with chemistry and writing.'[2]

He paid a high price for this idealism and for some time lived in considerable poverty with his wife and, eventually, nine children, finding it exceptionally difficult to earn a living from translating and writing alone.[3] It was not long, however, before his relentlessly enquiring mind began to gather the clues which led him to the discovery of a new form of medicine, one through which he felt able to do good rather than evil, to be a benefactor rather than a malefactor.

It was in the very year that he gave up his practice, while he was in the process of making a translation of the *Materia Medica* of the

Edinburgh physician, William Cullen, that Hahnemann made his first explicit observations about what he was eventually to call the homeopathic action of drugs. Following his translation of Cullen's description of the action of the eighteenth-century wonder drug cinchona (china or quinine), Hahnemann experimented with the drug on himself and discovered that the 'side' effects it brought about in patients were similar to the primary effects of malaria, the disease for which it was then the only known cure; he consequently speculated as to whether the explanation for the curative effect of the drug might lie in the similarity between the symptoms produced by both drug and disease, rather than in its 'tonic' effect on the stomach, as Cullen had suggested. From such a simple question emerged a revolution in medical thought.

Following this initial speculation, Hahnemann experimented with china in a way which was to become the standard method of making a homeopathic drug test, or 'proving' (from the German 'Prüfung' = 'experiment'), deliberately taking crude doses of the substance over a period of time, while observing the reactions in himself.[4] Satisfied that he could reproduce drug symptoms matching those of malaria by taking a controlled overdose of china, he began to test other contemporary drugs, such as belladonna, camphor and aconitum, and as a result of these experiments began to think seriously about a new medical principle, the principle of cure by similars.

THE BEGINNINGS OF HOMEOPATHY

It was to be six more years before, in 1796, he first formally articulated the single principle on which homeopathy is founded: 'Similia similibus curentur', traditionally, if inelegantly, translated as 'Let likes be treated by likes',[5] and shortly afterwards, in 1801, he resumed his medical practice, now basing it on this new homeopathic principle.[6] He continued to experiment with various substances, including such contemporary drugs as digitalis, opium, stramonium and valerian, and to think about the new medicine. In 1810 he published the first edition of the *Organon*,[7] the book in which he explained definitively what homeopathy entailed. Here he specifically established the similia principle as the bedrock of his medical practice, elaborating the notion that cure might be effected by the prescribing of small simple doses of medicine, chosen on the basis of the similarity of the symptoms produced by that medicine to the symptoms actually produced by the diseased person. In calling his new medical system 'homeopathy'('similar suffering') and orthodox medicine 'allopathy' ('opposite suffering'), he emphasised this important distinction between the two systems.

Eventually Hahnemann began to write about his experiments with these various medicinal substances: most of these provings were collected in the *Materia Medica Pura*[8] and formed the basis of many other such studies by other homeopaths following in his footsteps. His exploration did not stop here: he wrote prolifically on many aspects of medicine, constantly questioning, exploring and reworking his original ideas. Over the remaining thirty-three years of his life he revised the *Organon* five times, each time incorporating new discoveries or insights.[9] Hahnemann was an empiric – a scrupulous observer as well as an intuitive thinker – and he made haste slowly. Homeopathy was not born overnight in a flash of inspiration, but emerged gradually from over forty years of the study, experimentation and experience of this remarkable man. It emerged also from a good deal of conflict and opposition, its integrity maintained only by the persistence and dedication of its founder. Hahnemann's character was such that he was willing to stand up for what he believed to be true, and to work tirelessly to investigate and demonstrate this belief in the face of enormous opposition from the medical profession and from the apothecaries, the pharmacists of his day.

During the difficult period in which Hahnemann developed homeopathy, he and his little family were obliged to spend many years travelling from town to town in Saxony, always looking for a means of making a living, to allow him to continue his experiments and his thinking and writing. They lived in over twenty different places before eventually, in 1811, settling in Leipzig. Here Hahnemann at last practised and taught homeopathy for a number of years, until his success aroused the opposition of the university medical school and the apothecaries, who combined to force him into exile in the neighbouring duchy of Anhalt-Köthen in 1821.[10]

CONFLICTS WITH COLLEAGUES

As Hahnemann had studied, developed, practised and taught homeopathy for these ten years in Leipzig, so he had acquired students and disciples. Although his influence remained powerful, homeopathy was not for long restricted to the work of this one man: inevitably the increase in the number of homeopaths led to an increase in discussion and division. While some of his students hung on Hahnemann's every word and endeavoured to practise homeopathy exactly as he advised, others tried to adapt it to their own ideas and needs. From early in its history homeopathy was prone to internal fission, and the chief point of strain was Hahnemann's clear separation of homeopathic from allopathic medicine.

This aroused understandable opposition from some early homeo-paths: those who took up the new medicine had usually been trained in the old and often found it difficult to leave allopathic thinking behind. If they did not immediately succeed in curing a patient homeopathically they were inclined to revert to allopathic practices. However, it enraged Hahnemann when his students did not see that homeopathy and allopathy were intrinsically different, that the methods of allopathy were not complementary to those of homeopathy but antagonistic, suppressing symptoms and forcing them to find more inward expression rather than curing them. Hahnemann consequently became fierce in his promulgation and defence of the principles of his new medicine and alienated many potential allies by his insistence on 'pure' homeopathy.

Despite his rigour there developed a mongrel form of homeopathy ('bastard', Hahnemann called it, since it was, in his view, a union of base and noble), in which some homeopaths treated patients with drugs selected on the basis of a named disease, as in allopathy, while others tried to maintain the principle of selecting drugs on the basis of a more personal and idiosyncratic similarity to the whole of the patient's diseased condition. The deviants, called half-homeopaths or specificists, tended to prescribe drugs in very low dilutions, or even material doses, at a time when Hahnemann and others were already experimenting with extremely diluted substances and finding them effective. The now well-established split between low-potency 'specificist' and high-potency 'holistic' prescribers began at this very early date.[11]

NEW DEVELOPMENTS IN HOMEOPATHY

Hahnemann continued to elaborate his new system of medicine for many years, only gradually developing all the features which we now take for granted. In the very early stages he added to the principle of the simillimum that of the minimum dose. At first, this seemed to mean merely that the homeopath should use only as small a material amount of the drug as was necessary. However, it was not long before Hahnemann's persistent experimentation revealed that dilution and succussion of remedies somehow rendered them more effective; the term 'minimum dose' became used to refer not simply to small material amounts but to very attenuated and eventually even immaterial doses.[12] Many of his colleagues simply did not believe that a highly diluted medicine could be effective and they persisted in using remedies diluted only to a 3c – a still material dose – while Hahnemann himself (along with some of his more adventurous peers), was excitedly discovering the healing powers of remedies diluted up to 30c, a ridiculously small dose in the opinion of many.

Materialist doctors further took fright as Hahnemann began to develop the other non-materialist aspects of his science, to make explicit the vitalist philosophy which had always been inherent in homeopathy,[13] and to elaborate his important new theories about chronic disease, in which he suggested that most chronic disease was caused by the suppression of infections, specifically scabies and venereal disease.[14] Even though he was protected by the seclusion of Anhalt-Köthen, life was beginning to be difficult for Hahnemann in the early 1830s. Some of his younger colleagues in Leipzig began to express their opposition to the latest developments within homeopathy and Hahnemann became beleaguered and unhappy. His wife Johanna Henriette had died in 1829 and he found himself living a somewhat solitary life with his two youngest daughters, Charlotte and Luise.

LOVE AND MARRIAGE

However, in 1834, a completely unexpected change took place in his circumstances when the Marquise Melanie d'Hervilly, a 35-year-old Parisian feminist, artist and poet, came to Saxony to consult him. Having recently read the *Organon*, she was overwhelmed with enthusiasm for the new medicine. On meeting Hahnemann she extended her enthusiasm to its founder: the two fell in love and were married by January of the following year.[15] Within a few months Hahnemann left German-speaking territory for the first time in his life and went to live in Paris with his new wife. It was there, over the last nine years of his long and fruitful life, that he fully developed the practical implications of the observations he had recently made concerning vitalism and the origins of chronic disease.

PARIS

Initially, Hahnemann went to Paris in June 1835 simply as a private citizen, a retired doctor. Although he had applied to the French government for permission to practise medicine in Paris while still living in Saxony, he had been refused. Meanwhile, however, the Paris Society of Homeopaths had been pressing for official recognition and attempting to establish a homeopathic hospital and dispensary in Paris. M. Guizot, the powerful French Minister of Public Instruction, had therefore set up an official enquiry into the new medicine.[16] Although the conclusion of this enquiry was that homeopathy was a sham, just another unsubstantiated craze of the fashionable people, falling into the same category as mesmerism or phrenology, the minister himself became interested and admonished the French Academy of Medicine, whose members had returned this verdict, for their narrow-minded and unscientific attitudes:

'Hahnemann is a learned man of great worth. Science must be free for all. If homeopathy is a chimera, or a system without internal cohesion, it will collapse of its own accord; if, on the contrary, it represents progress, it will develop in spite of our protective measures and it is just that which the Academy must wish for above all, since its mission is to favour science and to encourage discoveries.'[17]

Encouraged by Guizot's attitude, Hahnemann made a second application for permission to practise. This was successful and he began his work in Paris with Melanie's assistance. What had begun as an extended holiday in the twilight of his life became an exciting and extraordinarily experimental period in the advancement of homeopathy. He was immediately welcomed to the city by the Parisian homeopaths and all seemed well. However, nothing is ever as it seems: he was soon to find that the splits and arguments he had known in Germany were not absent from France, and he was quickly embroiled in familiar controversies about the practice of pure homeopathy.

Since Hahnemann had first articulated the principles of homeopathy many years previously, knowledge of this medicine had spread far beyond Germany.[18] It had first reached Italy when Austria invaded Naples and the commander of the invading army took with him a certain Dr Necker, a homeopath. By the time Necker left Naples he had trained two accomplished Neapolitan doctors: Dr Romani and Dr de Horatiis, and through them homeopathy eventually reached the south of France. When the wife of Dr Des Guidi, a Neapolitan exile to Lyon, was cured by Dr Romani in Naples, Dr Des Guidi undertook the serious study of homeopathy and set up a practice in Lyon, thus becoming the first homeopath in France. A little later, in 1832, the English Dr Quin brought homeopathy to Paris: he had discovered it for himself while travelling on the Continent and had spent some time studying with Hahnemann before settling and practising for a while in Paris.

Hahnemann's earliest colleagues in the French capital were all members of the Société de Médecine Homoéopathique de Paris (The Paris Society), which had been in existence for about two years.[19] Its founder members, including Dr Simon, Dr Jourdan, Dr Curie, Dr Petroz and Dr Croserio, were struggling to establish homeopathy in Paris. Some two years earlier, the Society had awarded Hahnemann an honorary diploma, and its members had been overjoyed to receive him in their city, hoping that his presence would help their cause.

The pleasure of the Parisian doctors at having Hahnemann in their midst did not last, however. Gradually it became clear that some of them, at least, were not practising in the way Hahnemann demanded and he began to find his compeers more among the members of a second French homeopathic society, La Société Gallicane (The Gallic Society).[20] This had had its origins in 1832 in a meeting of six homeopaths at the house of Pierre Dufresne, and had been formally established the following year in Lyon under the presidency of Dr Des Guidi, with the intention of linking all French-speaking homeopaths: its chief members included Dr Peschier of Geneva as well as Dr Dessaix of Lyon.

Shortly after his arrival in Paris, Hahnemann was invited to become Honorary President of the Autumn Congress of the Gallic Society and, in his opening address to this conference, in September, he lambasted the members of the Paris Society in no uncertain terms, accusing them of being half-homeopaths.[21] Things became very difficult.

HAHNEMANN'S PRACTICE

All the same, and despite the ever-present politics of homeopathy, Hahnemann and his wife Melanie established a large and fashionable practice in their new home. This did much to remove homeopathy from obscurity and, for a while, set it firmly amid mainstream Western medicine. Freed from the strain of quarrelling with his Leipzig colleagues, and presented with numerous challenges to his skills in the shape of new patients, Hahnemann was able fully to put into practice the ideas he had been developing in Köthen. While in Paris he began to prescribe in quite a different way, using a great many new remedies and making extensive experiments with remedy potentisation, using far higher centesimal potencies than ever before and ultimately developing the LM potency.

Until the very end of his life he continued to observe and experiment. However, a life of continuous opposition had made him secretive and he allowed little to be published of the results of these last years' practice. This book is an attempt to uncover its true nature.

We have very little accurate information about Hahnemann's practice in general, let alone about its form in these last years. Previous studies have well described the preliminary stages of his search for a more rational system of healing, his discovery of the principles of homeopathy and his early practice of it. However, such descriptions have been based largely on Hahnemann's theoretical writings, because there has been very little evidence available concerning the practical application of his theories.

In many respects our knowledge of the way in which he actually prescribed has been founded on rumour. We have had little reliable information about it except what has been extracted from his published theoretical works by scholars such as Dudgeon,[22] Hughes[23] and Haehl.[24] These men painstakingly reconstructed the details of his prescribing by scouring the pages of his writings for 'therapeutic hints'. Tiny nuggets of advice have been extracted from the *Organon*, *Chronic Diseases*, the introductions to the several editions of his *Materia Medica* and his various learned articles, and we think we have gained some idea from these of how Hahnemann actually worked. In addition, from time to time, there have emerged a few brief references to his cases or descriptions of his practice by those who were with him while he was alive. A closer view of his practice and clearer evidence of his methods of treatment has been lacking, since the detailed records of his treatments of patients disappeared for many years after his death. However, they have recently come to light in Stuttgart, in the Robert Bosch Institute for the History of Medicine,[25] and we are now therefore in a position to gain new insights into Hahnemann's methods of practice throughout his life.

THE ROBERT BOSCH INSTITUTE

The treasure that is preserved in Stuttgart is unparalleled. Almost all Hahnemann's casebooks, from when he started to work as a homeopath in 1801, are to be found there. There are also some five thousand letters which were exchanged between him and his patients, as well as manuscript copies of his repertories and notebooks. Not only is material pertaining to Hahnemann stored there, but also the casebooks and notes of his great friend and colleague Baron Clemens von Boenninghausen, as well as numerous other documents and details concerning the early days of homeopathy.[26]

How all this material came to have been lost for so long and finally to have been collected here is a story in its own right. Hahnemann always intended that the writings documenting his later experiments should be made public in due course, but he was extremely concerned that this should not be done prematurely, at a time of crisis for homeopathy. Towards the end of his life, as he published increasingly controversial theories and attracted more attention to himself, he became wary of being misquoted or misunderstood and went to great lengths to try to prevent this. On his deathbed, he gave his wife the responsibility for publishing material from the casebooks and the text of the sixth edition of the *Organon*, which he had not long completed. However, he also asked her to delay that publication for a few years.[27] Melanie took her responsibilities in this matter seriously but was never able to fulfil the task entrusted to her, for a number of reasons.

At first, she was very busy. After Hahnemann's death her priority was to continue the Paris practice which they had established together, and she did this effectively for some time. However, she also had her own troubles; in 1849 she was prosecuted for practising while unqualified and thereafter had to practise under the cover of various doctors – first, with Charles Lethière, her ward, who had begun his professional career as a pharmacist and subsequently became a homeopathic doctor, and later with Dr Karl Boenninghausen (the son of Hahnemann's friend), who had married her adopted daughter, Sophie, in 1856. Her professional life was extremely busy and she appears never to have had either the time or the resources to settle down to publishing Hahnemann's material accurately, though she made several attempts both to supervise others and to find the time and space to do it herself.[28] She had corresponded with Baron von Boenninghausen in the 1860s about publication, but nothing came of this discussion before the Baron himself died in 1864.[29] Things became even more difficult after 1870, when war broke out between France and Prussia – the German Boenninghausens, Karl and Sophie, were obliged to leave Paris swiftly and Melanie went with them, taking all Hahnemann's documents to the Boenninghausen family estate in Darup, Westphalia. When Melanie herself returned to Paris, after only a short period of exile, the documents were left behind in Darup and remained there undiscovered until Dr Richard Haehl tracked them down after the end of the First World War.[30]

Even after this material had been discovered, its publication was still delayed, for Haehl had already completed his biography of Hahnemann and was only able to add to it a very few of the newly available details before it was published in 1922. He also managed to publish the sixth edition of the *Organon* for the first time.[31] Soon afterwards illness overtook him and he was unable to prepare any more material for publication before he died.

The documents were not lost, however. Robert Bosch, the German industrialist and philanthropist, acquired Haehl's entire collection of manuscripts and provided space for them, first in a small Hahnemann Museum based at Haehl's family home in Stuttgart, and later at the Homeopathic Hospital in Stuttgart. The collection survived the Second World War by being stored outside Stuttgart and was all but lost to sight until, in 1980, it made its way to the newly-founded Institut für Geschichte der Medizin, Robert Bosch Stiftung (the Robert Bosch Institute for the History of Medicine), established in the former lodge of the Bosch mansion in Stuttgart. There, now, this vast complete collection of Hahnemann's material is well looked after and catalogued, and once it has been fully studied there need no longer be speculation and rumour about the nature of Hahnemann's practice.[32]

We are thus, finally, able to discover the true nature of Hahnemann's practice from a study of his own original material. The excitement of such a study lies in two main aspects. The first is that it reveals the way in which Hahnemann's genius really operated – in the well-known infinite capacity for taking pains, taking risks, recording detail and making mistakes; and the second is in the way it makes clear the multiple misconceptions which have been built up around him and homeopathy through the oral transmission of information over the last 150 years.

In particular, such a study shows how Hahnemann altered his prescribing methods in his last years, in the light of his discoveries about both chronic disease and dynamisation. It shows the process by which he abandoned the use of the single unrepeated dry dose in favour of frequently-repeated liquid doses, and the way in which he made miasmatic prescribing a major part of his system, expanding on his earlier method of prescribing solely on the basis of characteristic symptoms. Because of the accidental sequestration of his material, most nineteenth and twentieth century homeopaths have developed their prescribing on the basis of what was known about Hahnemann's practice before he went to Paris – before he wrote the sixth edition of the *Organon*. The advances in the practical application of the homeopathic principles which Hahnemann made in the last few years of his life remained completely hidden until this final edition was published in 1921, nearly eighty years after his death.

Here he had made reference to these later techniques, but because its publication was delayed, very few homeopaths knew anything about them. Even when it was published, few homeopaths realised that it described the use of a wholly new potency, because the text was so obscure. It was not until Pierre Schmidt elucidated the text in the 1950s that most of the homeopathic world realised any part of what Hahnemann had been doing during his last years; and even so, the information remained quite theoretical in the absence of illustrative material from the casebooks.[33]

The present book is an attempt to describe and analyse the nature of this later practice in the last years of Hahnemann's life, and to discuss the process of Hahnemann's development in these hitherto shrouded years. The amount of available material is so extensive that this study can be no more than introductory. The collection includes fifty-four thick volumes containing the records of most of the patients Hahnemann had treated since 1801. There are thirty-seven volumes written in German between 1802 and 1835, and seventeen volumes written in French between 1835 and 1843 and later. (There were originally thirty-eight German volumes and eighteen French but the first volume in each series is missing.) After Samuel's death Melanie continued to practise by herself for a number of years at varying levels of intensity until her own death in 1878. Some of the Paris volumes contain exclusively material relevant to Melanie's solo practice. A full description and tabulation of the manuscripts is to be found in Appendix II.

This material is practically unknown, though some work has appeared in German. In 1964 Heinz Henne published texts of the first two surviving volumes of the Hahnemann casebooks.[34] They were intended to be the first in a series of the whole set of casebooks but, in fact, these two were the only volumes to be published. Hans Ritter, in a study of Hahnemann published in 1974, also made some limited use of this material.[35] One of the Institute's current researchers, Dr Walter Nachtmann, has published an article relating to Hahnemann's very early practice.[36] I myself have given a brief account of the practice in *A Homeopathic Love Story*.[37] 'Diplomatic' (i.e. verbatim) texts of all the surviving casebooks have now started to be published by Haug Verlag, Heidelberg, in a long-term project expected to take at least fifteen years from the publication of this present book.[38]

I have examined many of the surviving cases and extracted material from them to illustrate some of the main features of Hahnemann's method of practice at this time, as well as his use of remedies and potencies. I have tried to include as much detail as possible and to be as representative as possible in this, but clearly any personal selection from such a huge amount of material may exclude something of interest or significance to someone else. I have also included three complete cases as an Appendix: those of Mme Braun, M. Musard and Mme Lambert (pages 147–209). Mme Braun was one of Hahnemann's earliest patients and his treatment of her illustrates his methods in the early years in Paris. The orchestra leader M. Philippe Musard, while also an early patient of the Paris period, continued to be treated by Melanie after Samuel's death – his case thus spans a number of years and well illustrates some of the shifts in Hahnemann's prescribing practice. Mme Lambert came as a patient towards the very end of Hahnemann's life.

In writing this book I have not been in any way concerned to take sides in the apparently endless controversy between unicists and complexicists, classical and pathological prescribers. What I have tried to do as clearly as I can, is to present my impression of these last casebooks in order to bring some of the material into the light of day in an accessible manner, hoping that once attention has been drawn to it others may continue to study it in more depth.

I have been fascinated to discover the amount of experimentation and *ad hoc* solutions to which Hahnemann resorted, an approach so at odds with my previous understanding of his confident mastery. I have taken comfort from this, seeing more clearly the creative rather than the created Hahnemann. Of course Hahnemann still practises as we always thought he did, still does what he aways said he did – on the whole. What is interesting, however, is to see how often he broke his own rules, as do all creative people.

Because I have been looking at Hahnemann's *process* rather than his conclusion I have singled out the examples of his rule-breaking, but I do not mean to imply by this that he had no rules or that he always broke them, only that he allowed himself to do so in the interest of advancing his own learning.

NOTES

1. Richard Haehl has been his chief biographer. He published *Samuel Hahnemann, sein Leben und Schaffen*, in Leipzig in 1922. The English translation, *Samuel Hahnemann, His Life and Work*, (containing in the supplement some additional material, updating the details of Richard Haehl's personal collection of Hahnemann's papers), appeared in 1931. Haehl drew for his biography on some already published material, including the following: F. Albrecht, *Lebensbeschreibung von Hahnemann*, Leipzig 1851 (published anonymously) – A second edition was published under Albrecht's name in 1875: *Dr Samuel Hahnemanns Leben und Wirken, ein Gedenkbuch auf Grund von Familienpapieren*, Leipzig 1875; R. E. Dudgeon, *Lectures on the Theory and Practice of Homoeopathy*, London 1853; G. O. Kleinert, *Geschichte der Homöopathie*, Leipzig 1863; W. Ameke, *Die Entstehung und Bekämpfung der Homöopathie*, Berlin 1884, translated as *History of Homoeopathy* by A. E. Drysdale and ed. R. E. Dudgeon, London 1885; T. L. Bradford, *The Life and Letters of Dr Samuel Hahnemann*, Philadelphia 1895, as well as on unpublished letters and documents. In the years since the publication of his biography others have reworked the material he first fashioned, with varying degrees of success: A. S. Croll-Picard, *Hahnemann et l'homoéopathie*, Paris 1933; R. Waugh (later Hobhouse), *Life of C. S. Hahnemann*, London 1933; M. Gumpert, *Hahnemann, die abenteuerlichen Schicksale eines älterlichen Rebellen und seiner Lehre der Homöopathie*, Berlin 1934; R. Larnaudie, *La vie surhumaine de Samuel Hahnemann, fondateur de l'homoéopathie*, Paris 1935; R. Tischner, *Geschichte der Homöopathie*, published in four parts, Leipzig 1932–9; E. Verbaime, *Un certain Hahnemann*, Paris 1962, included some original material but did not give his sources for this; T. Cook, *Samuel Hahnemann*, Wellingborough 1981; H. Ritter, *Samuel Hahnemann*, Heidelberg 1974, was the first to add any reliable new material. He consulted the collection of manuscripts now housed in the Institut für Geschichte der Medizin, Stuttgart; H. J. Schwanitz, 'Homöopathie und Brownianismus, 1795–1844' in *Medizin in Geschichte und Kultur*, Vol. 15, Stuttgart 1983; R. Handley, *A Homeopathic Love Story*, California 1990 includes new material drawn from the collection in the IGM.

2. From Hahnemann's brief autobiographical notes, quoted in full in Haehl, *Samuel Hahnemann, His Life and Work*, Vol. 1, p. 64ff.

3. Hahnemann and his wife had eleven children in all, of whom

nine survived infancy: Henriette (1783), Friedrich (1786), Wilhelmina (1788), Amalie (1789), Karoline (1791), Ernst (1794, died three months later), Frederika (1795) and a stillborn twin, Eleanore (1803), Charlotte (1805), and Luise (1806).

4. Haehl, *op. cit.*, Vol. 1, pp. 36–7, quotes the details from Vol. 2, p. 108 of Hahnemann's translation of Cullen's *Materia Medica*: 'I took, for several days, as an experiment, four drams of good china twice daily. My feet and finger tips, etc., at first became cold; I became languid and drowsy; then my heart began to palpitate; my pulse became hard and quick; an intolerable anxiety and trembling (but without a rigor); prostration in all the limbs; then pulsation in the head, redness of the cheeks, thirst, briefly, all the symptoms usually associated with intermittent fever, as the stupefaction of the senses, a kind of rigidity of all joints, but above all the numb, disagreeable sensation which seems to have its seat in the periosteum over all the bones of the body – all made their appearance. This paroxysm lasted from two to three hours every time, and recurred when I repeated the dose and not otherwise. I discontinued the medicine and I was once more in good health.'

5. In 'Versuch über ein neues Prinzip zur Auffindung der Heilkräfte der Arzneisubstanzen', in Hufeland's *Journal*, Vol. 2, Nos. 2 and 3, 1796. Translated as 'Essay on a New Principle for Ascertaining the Curative Power of Drugs' in R. E. Dudgeon, *Lesser Writings*, London 1852, pp. 295–352.

6. This year also saw the publication of 'The Medicine of Experience,' an embryonic version of the *Organon*, included in Dudgeon, *op. cit.*, pp. 497–541.

7. S. Hahnemann, *Organon der rationellen Heilkunde*, Dresden 1810.

8. S. Hahnemann, *Reine Arzneimittellehre*, 6 vols., Dresden 1811–21 (1st edn), Dresden 1823–6 (2nd edn), Dresden and Leipzig 1830–3 (3rd edn). All remedies are subject to 'provings', controlled experiments in which the substance in question is taken repeatedly by a number of people (provers), who record all the changes in physical and emotional states which come about as a result. From an aggregate of the reported symptoms we get the homeopathic remedy picture which is the basis of a prescription.

9. In 1819, 1824, 1829, 1833 and 1842. This last version was not published until 1921. (See Bibliography for publication details.)

10. Legal action by the apothecaries resulted in Hahnemann's being forbidden to dispense his own medicines in Leipzig. However, this law did not extend to the neighbouring state of Anhalt-Köthen, whose

Duke was a friend and patient. The Duke appointed Hahnemann to be his court physician and thus afforded him some protection from the law.

11. A detailed historical analysis of this split will be found in H. Coulter, *Divided Legacy*, (4 vols.), Berkeley, California 1973, 1975, 1977, 1994.

12. For more detail about dosage and potencies see Chapters 8 and 9.

13. The vitalist philosophy declared that a spirit or energy other than matter resided in apparently material and inanimate things. Hahnemann first explicitly referred to the 'vital force' as a curative power in the 4th edition of the *Organon*, published in 1829.

14. See S. Hahnemann, *Chronic Diseases, passim* and *Organon*, 6th edition, paragraphs 78–81. See later, Chapter 3, for fuller discussion of the miasm theory.

15. For a full account of their meeting, marriage and life together see R. Handley, *A Homeopathic Love Story*, California 1990.

16. Specifically, he asked the French Academy of Medicine for a report on homeopathy. The report was produced on March 17th 1835 and asserted that homeopathy was 'full of numerous shocking contradictions' and 'many palpable absurdities'. 'Reason and experience are united to repel with all the force of intelligence a system like this.' (*Archives de la médecine homoéopathique*, Vol. 2 (1835), p. 396). And see also Coulter, *op. cit.*, Vol. 2, p. 547.

17. My translation. Quoted in Haehl, *op. cit.*, Vol. 1, p. 231.

18. For the early spread of homeopathy see G. R. Mitchell, *Homoeopathy*, London 1975.

19. The Paris Society was founded in 1832. It published a journal, *Archives de la médecine homoéopathique*.

20. The Gallic Society had also been in existence since 1832.

21. The speech is quoted in Haehl, *op cit.*, Vol. 2, p. 345.

22. R. E. Dudgeon, *Hahnemann's Therapeutic Hints*, London 1894.

23. R. Hughes, *A Manual of Pharmacodynamics*, 3rd edn London 1876; *A Manual of Therapeutics*, London 1877–8; *The Principles and Practice of Homoeopathy*, London 1902.

24. R. Haehl, *op. cit., passim*.

25. In the Institut für Geschichte der Medizin, Stuttgart.

26. There are some two hundred case books connected with the practices of Baron Clemens von Boenninghausen and his son, as well as over 1200 letters by various homeopathic doctors of the nineteenth and first half of the twentieth century. There are also 200 manuscripts from the estates of Dr G. A. B. Schweikert and Dr G. W. Gross. There

is a special library of the history of homeopathy with about 1200 books and 1400 periodicals. A printed catalogue of the library can be purchased from Buchhandlung für Medizin, Rüdigerstrasse 14, 70445 Stuttgart, Germany.

27. R. Haehl, *op. cit.*, Vol. 2, p. 458.
28. For a full account of these events see R. Handley, *op. cit.*
29. The correspondence is quoted in Haehl, *op. cit.*, Vol. 2, pp. 451–456. It exists in manuscript in the Institut für Geschichte der Medizin.
30. Haehl succeeded in buying Hahnemann's papers from the Boenninghausen family in 1920 with financial help from Dr Boericke. See Haehl, *op. cit.* Vol. 1, Preface. Dr Baur tells me that Dr James Willis Ward also contributed to the purchase of Hahnemann's papers.
31. R. Haehl (ed.), *Organon*, Stuttgart 1921.
32. Descriptions of the collection are to be found in H. Henne, 'Das Hahnemann-Archiv im Robert-Bosch-Krankenhaus in Stuttgart', *Sudhoffs Archiv*, Vol. 52 (1968); R. Wittern, 'The Robert Bosch Foundation and the Establishment of the Institute for the History of Medicine', *Clio Med*, December 15th 1978, Vols. 1 and 2, pp. 89–91.
33. P. Schmidt, 'The Hidden Treasures of the Last Organon', in *British Homoeopathic Journal*, July 1954, pp. 134–56.
34. H. Henne, (ed.), *Hahnemanns Krankenjournale*, Nos. 2 and 3, Stuttgart 1963.
35. H. Ritter, *Samuel Hahnemann: sein Leben und Werk*, Heidelberg 1974.
36. W. Nachtmann, 'Samuel Hahnemann als Arzt und Forscher, Wunschdenken und Wirklichkeit', in *Jahrbuch des Instituts für Geschichte der Medizin der Robert Bosch Stiftung*, Vol. 5, 1986, pp. 65–86.
37. R. Handley, *op. cit.*
38. Haug Verlag, Fritz-Frey-Strasse 21, 69121 Heidelberg, Germany.

Chapter 2

The Patients

The practice that Samuel and Melanie Hahnemann established in the heart of Paris soon became fashionable. The wealthy people of the city and, indeed, of Europe generally, were more than ready to try a new medicine, especially when its founder and most illustrious and eccentric practitioner was living in their midst with his intelligent and beautiful second wife. Almost immediately, the Hahnemanns began to see many patients – patients who came from all over Europe to seek help from the great homeopath whose fame had already spread far beyond Saxony.

Their patients were not limited to the wealthy but were drawn from all social classes and from most countries of the western world. They were, however, predominantly members of the French and British upper and professional classes: nobles, clergy, military officers, lawyers, doctors and teachers ... along with their wives and families. These were all people who, if they had been ill for long, had already had the doubtful advantage of extensive medical treatment, something scarcely likely to simplify Hahnemann's task of cure. With the less well-off patients, who had been unable to afford previous medical treatment, Hahnemann was more fortunate. Their illnesses were comparatively uncomplicated by allopathic treatment.

The Hahnemanns' first consulting rooms were in their first house in Paris, at No. 7 Rue Madame, a small house on the edge of the Luxembourg Gardens, to the south of the Seine. Here they saw patients for most of the day and then relaxed by strolling through the Gardens and going to the opera or the theatre. The British were among the earliest visitors: Lord Elgin, who had had a long-time connection with Paris, was quick to seek help for his chronic neuralgia and he brought his whole family. Lady Kinnaird represented the Scottish aristocracy. Several Scottish families began to consult them at this time, among them Mrs Erskine and her relatives, the Patersons and the Stirlings. Mrs Erskine was the first to come, complaining of serious and chronic gynaecological problems which had been unamenable to orthodox treatment. Mr Paterson followed later, bringing his son, Jacques Erskine Paterson. The Stirlings came even later and the Hahnemanns treated one of the daughters, Eliza, for many years for her mysterious and debilitating condition.

Another early British visitor was William Leaf, the London merchant who was to play such an important part in the establishing of homeopathy in Britain. He consulted the Hahnemanns about a bad skin condition. The Reverend Everest of Wickwar, an early apologist for homeopathy, was also a constant visitor. His complaints were legion. He travelled extensively abroad and used to call on the Hahnemanns frequently between journeys. The English homeopath Dr Quin consulted them, seeking help for his arthritis and the asthma brought on, he said, by quarrels with allopaths. Mrs Boddington began the influx of English women.

Many other distinguished residents of Paris also consulted the Hahnemanns in these early days: the sculptor, M. Auguste, who suffered from considerable rheumatic pain, and the very common tinnitus; the banker, Baron Rothschild, concerned about his arthritis and neuralgia. Three members of the Beugnot family, one of France's oldest families, consulted them: Viscount Beugnot, author of several historical works, his wife the Viscountess and his mother the Countess. M. Musard, the colourful leader of the most famous dance orchestra in Europe, consulted them about his gout and respiratory problems. M. Musard clearly recommended homeopathy to many other musicians, and several members of his own orchestra consulted the Hahnemanns: M. Guillon and M. Sy, the bassoonist, for example.

From elsewhere in France Dr Comte Sebastien Des Guidi was an early visitor, glad, no doubt, to have the opportunity of consulting a homeopath senior to himself. There were also many others whose names have not survived in history except in the pages of these case books. Mr Urchart came with high blood pressure; Mme Braun with menstrual and digestive problems; Mme Leloir with digestive and paralytic symptoms of some severity.

Sometime towards the end of 1836 the Hahnemanns moved to a much grander house, north of the Seine, in the newly-built Rue de Milan, on the way to what was then the outlying village of Montmartre. Only a few years earlier sheep had been grazing where the Hahnemanns now lived. The railways had yet to be built and the Gare St Lazare, which soon imposed its character on the area, had not yet been begun. Even here, and perhaps especially here, the rich and fashionable came to visit, blocking the roads with their queues of carriages.[1]

The British continued to come in large numbers, often staying at the Hotel Bristol, a little England in the centre of Paris: The Gainsboroughs, Ferdinand de Vere, Lord Capel (later Lord Essex), Lady Belfast and Lady Drummond, the Duchess of Melford, kept up the aristocratic influx, while the established middle-classes were represented by Mr Campbell, who had already consulted Dr Quin about his mercurial eruptions; the Buchanans and the Bosanquets (connections of the Erskine-Patersons), and Master Lindsay Couts. Mr Charles French, an English teacher resident in Paris, came about recurrent bouts of venereal disease, the hypochondriac Mr Wright came repeatedly. Mr Robert Lyster, a 'man of letters' with severe gout and problems arising after venereal disease, was also a constant visitor. Miss Trotter, Mrs Osborne and Mrs Butler-Johnstone kept up the presence of British women.

The French aristocracy did not waver in their support. In the later years of the practice we find such figures as Mme la Marquise de Villers; the historian the Comte de Tocqueville and his wife; M. le Comte de Quelin; M. le Comte Chabert de Fonville; the 19-year-old Marquis de Fayal, the Comte de Carlaxo and the Comte de Louvencourt. We also encounter the names of some of the permanent emigré population of Paris, the Viennese M. Pierre Yermaloff and the Russian historian Prince Galitzin, whose descendants remain staunch supporters of homeopathy.

As the number of homeopathic doctors increased, so they too came to consult Hahnemann: Dr Dunsford came from Rome where he had been practising, and brought with him his 19-year-old daughter. Dr Croserio, Paris's leading homeopath, came with his wife and daughter. Another Parisian, Dr Deleau, came on two separate occasions. The first time he came he was not a homeopath and was too nervous to take the medicine prescribed. He returned a few years later, now himself a homeopath, and this time agreed to take the remedy. After Hahnemann's death, he, along with Dr Croserio, became one of Melanie's chief supporters and assistants.

Creative artists came in profusion: the essayist M. Legouvé; the sculptor David d'Angers; the novelist Eugène Suè; the musician Frederic Kalkbrenner and his family; the Böhrers Max and Anton, a famous contemporary string duo; Nicolo Paganini, the renowned violinist; the painter M. Lalaisse; the sculptor M. Etex and the great composer Cherubini. Actors and singers continued to be well represented. The singer Theodore and the famous Spanish singing family Garcia brought their sore throats and laryngitis. Perhaps the most famous of these performing artists was Mlle Rachel, the acting sensation of Paris, who consulted the Hahnemanns about her stage-fright. The noted theatre critic M. Castil Blaze was a patient. Other less notable patients were the working professionals staffing the Paris theatres and vaudevilles: M. Julienne de Turmeny; M. Toussaint; M. Rousselot; the singer M. Schianski; the pianist Martial Minviel; M. Wartel; M. Sordo of the Opera. That now out-of-date occupation of 'man of letters' was represented by men such as M. Escure. All these and hundreds more whose reputation has not outlasted them were eager visitors to the Paris consulting rooms.

There were even a few visitors from Canada and America, both North and South, reflecting the fact that homeopathy had already spread to those parts. From New York came the lawyer Mr Mowatt, presumably related to Anna Cora Mowatt, the actress who has left an account of her visit to the Hahnemanns. Miss Orville Devey and Miss de Schoyer also came from New York. Colonel Pinheiro Ferreira came from Peru and there was a small Brazilian contingent. There were, however, no visitors from Pennsylvania, where Constantine Hering and his colleagues had recently established the first homeopathic medical school.

THE CONSULTATION

Once admitted to the house, the patients were invited to sit in a spacious anteroom where numerous people waited to see the great homeopath. Eventually, ushered into the consulting room, they found Melanie seated at the writing table and Samuel in an armchair, probably smoking his long pipe, a habit of which Melanie never managed to break him. The room was lined with books, clocks and pictures. Melanie frequently took the initial details of the case, usually both speaking and writing in French. When she had taken the history, and the patient had come to a stop in his or her own account, Hahnemann would then apparently take up the questioning, asking more specific, sometimes even leading, questions about such things as the nature of the stool or the nature of the pain, seeking for more detail in modalities. He seems to have added notes of the answers to the record, often inserting them between the lines or in the margins. Like Melanie, he normally spoke and wrote in French though there was an occasional lapse into German.[2] The handwriting of the case books reflects this pattern. In most cases the bulk of the writing was done by Melanie and comments were added by Samuel.[3]

It is not clear how long the initial case taking would have lasted. At one point in his career, Hahnemann wrote that he saw patients for an hour and a half on their first appointment. This might have been necessary in some of the cases recorded in these books: Prince Galitzin, the emigré Russian prince who wrote a history of Paris, for example, gave an extremely detailed history, from which we learn that his father suffered badly from abscesses and his mother died of pulmonary tuberculosis, as did one of his uncles and three of his nephews. M. Pierre Yermaloff of Vienna also came with a long history: one and a half pages are devoted to the details of his previous illnesses. He had had treatments, both orthodox and homeopathic, in Austria, France, Germany and Russia. He had also seen no less than seven Parisian doctors. Paganini, who visited them not long before he died, revealed many horrific details of his previous extensive treatments at his first appointment.

In many cases, however, the details taken down at the initial appointment were quite few and it is scarcely likely that the interview which produced them would have taken as long as an hour and a half, unless there were lengthy unrecorded social exchanges. The initial notes are usually restricted to a few lines and rarely exceed a page. Many patients brought letters from previous medical advisors describing earlier vicissitudes in health. Such letters are often attached to the casebook and usually provide details of past treatments. Mrs Erskine and her Scottish friends all brought letters, as did many of the British patients. Mme Maurice, who moved around France with her customs officer husband, corresponded with the Hahnemanns frequently. In these cases an extremely detailed case history would not always have been necessary.

Nevertheless we do have to acknowledge that the case taking was not as detailed as we might expect from the description in the *Organon*,[4] though it proceeded on much the same lines. Presumably, by the time he had settled in Paris, Hahnemann had become so skilled at case taking that he knew more precisely than before what detail he needed. He was interested in rather different details from those which preoccupy most modern practitioners. His emphasis was on current symptoms, and by symptoms he meant only 'deviations from health'. He was interested secondarily in the 'history of (the patient's) complaints'. Details such as the nature of the stool, the sleep pattern, the temperature, thirst and sweat in fever, the nature of menstruation in women, as specified in the *Organon*, are noted with great regularity. The disposition of the patient, precipitating causes of the disease, living habits and diet were all also the subject of enquiry. It is clear that Hahnemann was interested from the outset in particularising the disease process in the patient, in looking for characterising features of the disease. Notably absent from his case notes are details in some of the areas which a modern homeopath is very careful to investigate – family history and constitution for example, or any extensive consideration of character or psychological orientation.

THE ILLNESSES

Details of the patients' past medical history, both their illnesses and treatments, vary in scope and intensity. Many patients had been chronically ill for years, especially with venereal disease. The orchestra leader M. Musard mentioned having had a chancre years ago. The sculptor M. Auguste had had a chancre. Mr. Lyster had amaurosis and gout, which seem to have begun after venereal disease. The Scottish Mr Campbell had had syphilis, M. Persin and M. Hubert gonorrhoea. M. Dupont and M. Gartempe had had both syphilis and gonorrhoea. Almost all the women had 'fleurs blanches', the 'whites' or leucorrhoea, the polite term used to describe a vaginal discharge which may or may not have been diseased. Several women were said to have contracted venereal disease from their husbands: Mme de Champagny, Mme Racine, Mme Drigon and Mme Rafton were among these.

Phthisis (tuberculosis) and unclearly differentiated chest and lung complaints were frequent. Although phthisis had not yet reached its peak it is strongly represented. We follow the sufferings and treatments of M. Lecointe, Mme de Grisy, Mme Lebauche, M. Marion and M. Lascour. Mme Berthou came two months after recovering from pneumonia, still troubled by a persistent cough. Dr Quin suffered from asthma. M. Auguste suffered from constant coughing and spitting since having a catarrh.

Rheumatic and gouty complaints were constant. M. Auguste, M. Musard, Mr Lyster, Dr Quin, David d'Angers, Eugène Suè and Baron Rothschild had all suffered from pain in the joints and limbs for many years.

Even more common were digestive complaints. In England dyspepsia was called the 'Victorian Malady', and it was clearly no less rife at this time in Paris. This is scarcely to be wondered at in view of the general level of diet and the steady use of alcohol and drugs, of whose danger few seem to have been informed. Dreadful digestive and bowel problems, especially constipation, are frequently mentioned and the taking of powerful laxatives was habitual. Patients constantly report their use of enemas. The Lyon homeopath, Dr Des Guidi, was in terrible pain with frequent diarrhoea. M. Auguste suffered from bloody diarrhoea. M. Garnot and M. Camus had 'always' been constipated. M. Arles Dufour had been poisoned by eating Duc Homard. M. Klein had had dysentery for two years, apparently after drinking a lot of iced water.

Nervous complaints were also frequent, among both men and women. These ranged from the ill-defined and ill-understood 'neurasthenic' states of weakness, trembling and palpitations suffered by Mme Graundin, M. Musard, M. Gotard, Vicomte Beugnot, Mlle Langston and Mme de St. Cloud to the melancholy and mania of M. Scipio de Thionville and the apparent schizophrenia of Mlle Sheila Brugmann and Master Lindsay Couts. Mme la Marquise de Villers was subject to alarming losses of reason before periods, and Mme Bournichon experienced extreme attacks of melancholy, desiring to die and even to kill herself.

There were heart complaints: M. Legouvé suffered from these, as did Mme Ladarnière and Mme Croserio.

There were multiple skin disorders: itches, rashes, spots, scabs, pustules, erysipelas, ulcers, chancres, condylomata, polyps and wens. M. Collmann and Mr Leaf suffered from the ubiquitous 'exanthème' or rash, while M. Chauchot suffered from polyps. Mme Roquin reported that she had had scabies at birth. Mme Rafton had had it for eight months at the beginning of her marriage.

Gynaecological problems were legion: Mme Bournichon suffered from sycotic vegetation around the neck of the uterus; Mme Laplace had difficulty with her periods, pain and vomiting twenty-five times a day. Mme Bagdazar had heavy periods twice a month.

There were headaches: Count Schowaloff had had migraine for ten years. Mlle de Baunaud had frequent headaches with rushes of blood to the head. The Portuguese diplomat Gabriel de Marsarelles gave a graphic account of the zigzag aura associated with the onset of his migraines.

There were fevers: Mme Mayard, Mme Clouzet and Mme Aubertin had had intermittent fevers. Marie Legouvé had scarlet fever. Vicomtesse Beugnot had had malarial fever in Naples. Many patients had been affected by the cholera outbreak of 1832.

Wounds and injuries were relatively common, rather different in character from those with which a modern doctor becomes familiar. M. de Simencourt had been almost blinded by a cerebral fever following a fall from his horse. M. le Comte de Quelin had had a powder flask explode in his face twelve years previously and his eyes had troubled him ever since. M. Aussandon had had problems with his digestion ever since his entrails had been torn out by a bear.

THE TREATMENTS

We get a grim picture of the state of orthodox medicine from these patients' accounts of their previous treatments. Bleeding and leeching were still common, as were massive doses of drugs and fairly primitive surgical intervention. Doctors also used various methods of irritating the skin in order to draw an assumed inflammation away from its original site in the body: they used *ventouses* or cupping glasses, to apply suction to a part, *vésicatoires* to cause blisters and *sétons* (needles threaded with resined horse hairs drawn through the skin and left there to cause suppuration) for the same purpose. Hahnemann himself cites some of the many drugs used for a variety of different reasons: 'calomel, corrosive sublimate, mercurial ointment, nitrate of silver, iodine and its ointments, opium, valerian, cinchona bark and quinine, foxglove, prussic acid, sulphur and sulphuric acid, perennial purgatives . . .'[5]

The patients reported not only the treatment they had had, but frequently also the names of their previous doctors. Naturally such mentions were rarely complimentary or the patients would not now have been consulting Hahnemann. M. le Comte de Louvencourt had been treated by the notorious François Joseph Broussais and had been ill ever since. The famous Dr Marjolin had taken out a polyp from Mme Lewis's womb: afterwards there had been inflammation of the sexual parts. Marjolin had also played a part in the confusing gynaecological treatment of Mme Laplace. After various unsatisfactory diagnoses of her condition a Dr Moreau had diagnosed a fibroid tumour as big as an egg. However, a Mme Barvini, presumably a midwife, had recently examined Mme Laplace and found no evidence of this. Dr Magendie had diagnosed M. Sabatier as having hypertrophy of the heart and had treated him with iodine, digitalis and morphine, which had made him very ill. He had then been treated with leeches and cupping, but this treatment had brought on rheumatic pains and palpitations.

Many patients had already been treated homeopathically by other doctors. The Parisian doctors Petroz, D'Oroszko, Bolléaman, Molin, Simon and Davet are mentioned frequently, often none too favourably. The continuing problem that Hahnemann had with doctors who did not practise homeopathy in the way he advocated surfaces in his attitude to some of these homeopaths. In particular he seems to note the failures of Dr Petroz with some persistence. Patients from other parts of France had fared better with Dr Des Guidi from Lyon, Dr Mabit from Bordeaux or Dr Peschier from Geneva. Some had consulted homeopaths in other parts of the world: Dr Dunsford, Dr de Horatiis, Dr Scudere and Dr Romani in Italy; Dr Roth, Dr Kopff, Dr Aegidi and Dr Wieske in Prussia; Dr Bukhamian in Russia and Dr Hull and Dr Gram in New York.[6] The number of doctors mentioned by name brings home to us with some clarity the way in which homeopathy was establishing itself little by little in pockets all over Europe and America.[7]

On the whole, Hahnemann seems to have responded to all these patients without judgement. He recorded merely the facts of their cases with only minimal addition of opinion or comment. We get very little sense of the personality of either Hahnemann or his wife through the records: the homeopaths' personalities do not colour their representation of the patient. In this the case notes are quite unlike those of Dr Des Guidi, which are strewn with entertaining personal asides and comments.[8]

Hahnemann did, however, occasionally venture a comment about certain patients. He cut M. Lecointe's smoking down, for example, from 10–24 cigars daily to one pipe only and recorded that, although the young man denied continuing the habit, his father reported that he was smoking a lot. When he was clearly becoming slightly impatient with Miss Sheila Brugmann, who frequently screamed intermittently for an hour or more, Melanie told her that if she did not stop screaming she would get a goitre. Hahnemann also occasionally commented that a certain patient was incurable. Of the 29-year-old Mme de Vallière, who came suffering from pulmonary tuberculosis, he wrote that she was incurable and that he had only agreed to treat her out of compassion. He saw her nearly every day for several weeks. In September 1840 he reluctantly accepted a Mme Morrisse as a patient, writing that she was treated 'without hope' and only because she insisted: 'Elle le veut absolument'. Her insistence was rewarded – Hahnemann treated her frequently and very experimentally, and she was still coming to see him and maintaining an equilibrium in her health when he himself died in June 1843!

Hahnemann rarely turned a patient away, although there are one or two examples of his doing this. He recorded no prescription for M. Gotard but did not explain why. He sent a M. Teste on to Dr Croserio for treatment for no very apparent reason. Sometimes he made his reason plain: he was quite reluctant to treat Mme Graundin when she first came in 1836 because he thought she was an incurable hypochondriac, and noted how many other doctors she had seen. He told her very clearly that she would need to come to him for two years. His character assessment was justified, for she left him after a few treatments only to return two years later having been treated by Dr Mollin meanwhile. Hahnemann did not prescribe for her on this occasion and she did not come back to him.

Hahnemann's charges varied. He had a range of fees which he seems to have adjusted – whether to the means of the patient or to the difficulty of the case is not clear. The fees are not often recorded in the case books, and when they are, various amounts are specified. M. Cotran, a lamplighter, paid only 10 francs. M. Hermans, the cornet player, paid 10 francs a time for his treatment for gonorrhoea. M. Duchine paid 20 francs. M. Guillon, a musician in Musard's orchestra, paid 50 francs. M. Rivière paid 50 francs per month. M. Gaston, an actor at the Comédie Française, paid 100 francs at his first appointment. M. Delille paid 100 francs, 'gibt hundert' in one of Hahnemann's rare lapses into his native language. Viscount d'Auteuil paid 200 francs, while the affluent M. Musard was charged 300 francs.

As we have seen, Hahnemann treated most of his patients from his own consulting rooms, only occasionally making house calls in the evenings on patients who were unable to visit him. We also know that he was not averse to treating patients by letter, as many of these letters survive. He also treated several family members through the report of the one who had come to the consulting room. There are frequent marginal prescriptions for the wives, husbands or children of patients. He clearly encouraged self-prescribing to some degree. Those who were knowledgeable, such as M. Arles Dufour and the Reverend Everest from England, prescribed for themselves quite persistently. He seems to have assumed that very many of his patients had remedies at home and recorded incidental examples of self, or intra-familial prescribing about which he was told. Sometimes he participated in such prescribing, as when Max Böhrer treated his mother with Sulphur: this had ameliorated her migraine at first but had now stopped acting. Hahnemann was happy to send on higher potencies. Paganini reported that Mr Loveday, with whom he was staying, had given him Ipecac., but that it had not helped. (Nothing helped Paganini.) Mlle Denis had got hold of some Rhododendron from Marie Ganneron. Hahnemann's patients were clearly not inhibited about treating themselves in acute conditions.

In his relationships with his patients we see Hahnemann taking on all comers. Some came once or twice and never returned, whether cured or disillusioned we shall never know. Most came for several treatments and left feeling somewhat better. Many came repeatedly over periods of years, coming to see the Hahnemanns as their general physicians and getting deeply involved in the homeopathic way of life, trusting Hahnemann through all.

NOTES

1. A description of a visit to Hahnemann's consulting rooms written by Anna Cora Mowatt has survived and is printed in T. L. Bradford, *The Life and Letters of Dr Samuel Hahnemann*, Philadelphia 1895, pp. 384–95.
2. In the case of M. Schoeppingk, a young German boy of 12, Hahnemann wrote for over half a page in German before Melanie took over. Presumably Hahnemann began the case-taking on this occasion in order to put the boy at ease in his own language. Elsewhere there are occasional lapses into German.
3. I infer this from the appearance of the manuscripts. Frequently the first interview appears to have been recorded mainly in Melanie's hand, with additional notes by Hahnemann. This is especially true in the early years of the Paris practice. Sometimes the whole case or the whole of one interview is written in Hahnemann's hand, sometimes in Melanie's. Clearly they often saw patients together and sometimes saw them alone. When the bulk of the case is written in Melanie's hand, Hahnemann's additions have the appearance of being records of supplementary questions, looking for clarification or specific detail. This pattern can be observed in the plates.
4. S. Hahnemann, *Organon*, (6th edn), paragraphs 82–99.
5. Hahnemann, *op. cit.*, paragraph 74. For further details of contemporary medical treatment, see the *Organon* throughout and Chapter 7.
6. Dr Petroz was the president of the Paris Homeopathic Society with which Hahnemann fell out early after his arrival in Paris. Hahnemann reported in his case books that Petroz had given Mme Bourdon Belladonna for a 'rhume' which had lasted a year. All it had done was stop the cough. He had also unsuccessfully treated Master Albert

Duchinon with Arsenicum and Bovista. He had failed with M. Pacon. Mlle Ganneron had got worse under his treatment. M. Gotard had also been treated by Petroz who gave him Anacardium, Aurum and Agaricus without improvement. (Hahnemann himself only saw Gotard once and did not prescribe.) M. Rousselot had been treated unsuccessfully by both Dr Petroz and Dr Bolléaman.

Dr d'Oroszko had treated Mlle Ganneron, with whom Petroz had failed. D'Oroszko had also treated the Vicomtesse de St Amaro with a number of remedies and she had had a cough since his treatment. He had treated M. Gibert, the tobacco merchant and Mlle Alise d'Arsay, both badly, according to Hahnemann's comment. Dr Léon Simon, another prominent Parisian homeopath, had treated Mme Michal for a year without success. He had also treated M. Garnot for four months for constipation. Dr Davet had treated M. Cherubini, the distinguished composer. Dr Molin had treated Mme Bournichon homeopathically with Sulphur, Belladonna, Stannum, Thuja, Aurum, Nitric Acid, Lycopodium and Nux Vomica. He had also given Mme de la Nois Arsenicum and China without effect.

Dr Maingot, from Abbéville, had treated Louise Flouest's persistent cough with Calcarea Carbonica and Sulphur. Dr Dessaix, from Lyon, had treated Mme de la Roche. Dr Des Guidi had treated M. Dellmar and Mrs Elisabeth Campbell in Lyon. Dr Peschier in Geneva had treated the law student M. Hubert, from Tours, and also the elder Mme Rolland Gosselin. He had given her medicines which were too strong, and since treatment she had been troubled with irritation of the womb. M. Auguste had seen Drs Davet, Wieske and Hoffmann already.

Dr Quin had treated Mr Campbell in London. He and Dr Necker in Lucca had both treated Prince Galitzin. Dr Dunsford had treated Lord Capel (later Lord Essex) frequently in Rome. From 1838 Capel had treatment from Hahnemann while in Paris and from Dr Quin while in London. Dr Dunsford had also treated the Reverend Everest, who had seen many doctors in the course of his eventful life. The singer Schianski had seen Dr Aegidi in Prussia and Dr Bukhamian in Russia. Mr Wright had been given Aconite and Nux Vomica by Dr Scudere in Italy. Dr de Horatiis, from Naples, had treated Miss Trotter. Dr Hartung had treated Mme la Baronne Sophie Bender in Milan. Dr Wieske had treated Mme Frederic Ganneron. Dr Roth had treated the young Scottish boy, Lindsay Couts, with Nux Vomica.

Dr Gram, the homeopath of Danish origin who had brought homeopathy to America in 1824, had treated the lawyer Mr Mowatt of New York. Mr Mowatt had also been treated in Bremen by a Dr

Cruncher. Miss Orville Devey, visiting from New York, had been recommended by Dr Hull, an influential homeopath there. Miss de Schoyer, another New Yorker, had also been treated by Dr Hull.

7. The evidence from Hahnemann's casebooks of the worldwide activity of homeopaths at this time may be supplemented by the list given in the introduction to F. H. Quin, *Pharmacopeia*, London 1834. In this he lists over 300 homeopaths (not to mention five vets!) practising in 1834 in areas now known as Austria, North America, South America, the Czech and Slovak Republics, Scandinavia, England, France, Germany, Greece, Hungary, Italy, Poland, Russia, Sicily and Switzerland.

8. See J. Baur, *Les manuscrits du Docteur Comte Sebastien Des Guidi*, Vols. 1 and 2, Lyon 1985, 1986.

Chapter 3

The Theory of Disease

CHRONIC DISEASE

Even this cursory glance at Hahnemann's clientele will already have made it clear that the problems he would have had to face in treating these patients were in many ways quite different from those faced by a modern homeopath. They were probably also quite different from those he himself had faced for much of his life in Saxony. It is a commonplace of medical history that a society creates its own diseases, and this is very clearly demonstrated in the descriptions of the sufferings of Hahnemann's patients. Although we see examples of digestive, muscular-skeletal, respiratory and cardiovascular problems which might well be found in the practice of any modern physician, there were also many problems which were more characteristic of the early nineteenth century in Europe, (and, moreover, of an early nineteenth-century capital city), than they are of today's (European) population or of the population of rural Saxony. Eruptive skin diseases, phthisis, frank and latent venereal disease, the effects of cholera, malaria, smallpox and typhoid are all more visible here than the allergies, cancer, post-viral fatigue syndrome and auto-immune diseases which have become common in modern times. Convulsive and paralytic conditions were especially rife and a deep fatigue (probably due to undiagnosed anaemia) affected a great many patients.

Fortunately, since homeopathy treats the patient and not the disease, the fact that Hahnemann treated rather different manifestations of disease from those presented to modern homeopaths does not limit the interest of his procedures as much as it might for practitioners of another medical discipline. In any case, as Hahnemann would have been the first to say, the apparently new diseases which we observe in modern society are not new at all; they are simply fresh manifestations of that age-old disease, psora, to which he had attributed most of the diseases of humanity, not very long before he came to Paris.[1]

Hahnemann saw the illness he encountered in the French capital as a challenge to his new medical system, and was excited to have the

33

opportunity to experiment so thoroughly with the implications of his recently-formulated theory of disease. In this he had divided disease into two categories, acute and chronic. For him acute diseases were 'rapid disease processes . . . [which] run their course and come to an end more or less quickly,'[2] while chronic diseases were those which arose 'from the dynamic contagion of a chronic miasm.'[3] Among acute diseases (or acute miasms) he included febrile conditions, epidemic diseases and diseases such as smallpox, measles, yellow fever and cholera. Among chronic diseases (or chronic miasms) he included psora, syphilis and gonorrhoea. as well as iatrogenic diseases – those induced by medical treatment. Acute disease would, if untreated, end in either spontaneous recovery or relatively rapid death. Chronic disease, if untreated, would take a progressively stronger hold on the organism of the patient, causing various kinds of symptoms of illness and ending, eventually, with death.

Hahnemann initially used the word 'miasm' to refer to what we would now call infectious disease. The term was originally used in the eighteenth and nineteenth centuries to convey the sense that disease, especially fever, was transmitted in a miasm, a misty cloud which hung around infected people or places – marshes or hospitals were favourite sites.[4] Hahnemann himself had used the word in this way when he explained how the cholera infection, or miasm, was transmitted, in his essay 'On the Mode of Propagation of the Asiatic Cholera'. Here Hahnemann suggested that cholera was transmitted by tiny disease-bearing creatures which clung in a miasm to sailors' beards and leapt off in other continents. Both the disease and the means of its transmission seem to be included in the term 'miasm': . . . 'On board ships . . . the cholera miasm finds a favourable element for its multiplication, and grows into an enormously increased brood of those excessively minute, invisible, living creatures, so inimical to human life, of which the contagious matter of the cholera most probably consists – on board these ships . . . this concentrated aggravated miasm kills several of the crew; the others, however, being frequently exposed to the danger of infection and thus gradually habituated to it, at length become fortified against it and no longer liable to be infected. These individuals, apparently in good health, go ashore, and are received by the inhabitants without hesitation into their cottages, and ere they have time to give an account of those who have died of the pestilence on board the ship, those who have approached nearest to them are suddenly carried off by the cholera. The cause of this is undoubtedly the invisible cloud that hovers closely around the sailors who have remained free from the disease, and which is composed of probably millions of those miasmatic animated beings, which, at first developed on the broad marshy banks of the tepid Ganges, always searching out in preference the human being to his destruction and attaching themselves closely to him . . .'[5]

Initially, Hahnemann's theory of disease merely postulated that chronic disease was initiated by such specific infections, and primarily by psora, the itch disease, which, he suggested, manifested in many different forms: . . . 'Not only most of the many cutaneous eruptions . . . which have received separate names, but also almost all adventitious formations, from the common wart on the finger up to the largest sarcomatous tumour, from the malformations of the finger-nails up to the swellings of the bones and the curvature of the spine, and many other softenings and deformities of the bones . . . are caused by the Psora. So, also, frequent epistaxis, the accumulation of blood in the veins of the rectum and the anus, discharges of blood from the same . . . haemoptysis, haematemesis, haematuria, and deficient as well as too-frequent menstrual discharges, night sweats of several years duration, parchment-like dryness of the skin, diarrhoea of many years standing, as well as permanent constipation and difficult evacuation of the bowels, long-continued erratic pains, convulsions occurring repeatedly for a number of years, chronic ulcers and inflammations, sarcomatous enlargements and tumours, emaciation, excessive sensitiveness as well as deficiencies in the senses; excessive as well as extinguished sexual desire; diseases of the mind and of the soul, from imbecility up to ecstasy, from melancholy up to raging insanity; swoons and vertigo, the so-called diseases of the heart; abdominal complaints and all that is comprehended under hysteria and hypochondria . . . are . . . true descendants of this many-formed Psora alone.'[6]

This categorisation of illnesses included under the umbrella-term 'psora' has often been criticised as being too general to be helpful, since it appears to cover all the diseases known to humanity. However, Hahnemann's main concern was to demonstrate that psora was not simply a surface or skin disease, but one which first permeated the whole organism, only then manifesting its characteristic skin affections. The psoric miasm, like an acute miasm such as measles, was a whole-body illness in which the skin eruptions were the last symptoms to appear. He argued that as long as the skin eruption was allowed to remain as the focus of expression of the disease no further harm would come to the patient, but that once the skin eruption had been suppressed, as it commonly was, and the primary locus of disease expression removed, then the organism would have to find another such locus, and the appearance of any of the diseases named above might therefore be the consequence of the suppression of the manifestations of psora on the skin.

In a larger way, Hahnemann also seems to have implied that the original historical suppression of this most primitive form of expression of disease was the basis for the growth of all further disease. Psora, he suggested, was the original human disease, manifesting in the world as skin disease. It had gained its frightening hold over humankind through the widespread and centuries-long practice of the suppression of skin eruptions, traditionally by means of sulphur baths and applications. Such suppression had caused the organism to find another focus of expression for the disease, and this was frequently more damaging than the original skin eruption. Psora was now expressed not only in leprosy, scabies and other skin affections, but also in diseases located in more internal organs and systems.[7] It was the chronic illness underlying the scabies (or itch) eruption, and became the morbid soil in which disease of a more complicated and flourishing kind was later able to grow. At a later stage other virulent diseases, such as syphilis and gonorrhoea, grafted themselves onto a population already made susceptible by psora: this resulted in other miasms called 'syphilis' and 'sycosis' (after the fig-like (sycotic) growths characteristic of gonorrhoea).

Hahnemann first propounded this theory of disease to his closest colleagues, Dr Stapf and Dr Gross in 1827, after having worked on it in private for some twelve years. The two men were horrified, fearing that such a wild idea would bring further contempt upon a homeopathy already scoffed at because of the smallness of its doses. They pleaded with him not to publish it. However, for Hahnemann it had now become the bedrock of his medical theory: he could not suppress an explanation of disease which seemed to him to hold out the promise of a means to cure it. He published the ideas in *Chronic Diseases* in 1828, and shortly afterwards began to introduce into his practice methods of prescribing which were the consequence of the new theory.

Hahnemann's miasm theory, as it has become known, has been a difficulty for homeopathic practitioners ever since. Some have responded like Stapf and Gross, with embarrassment; others have seen it as the most brilliant contribution of homeopathy. Early English writers such as Dudgeon and Hughes were outright in their condemnation of it, while early Americans such as Allen and Kent seized upon it as the missing element in an otherwise perfect science. To this day many practitioners ignore it while others make it the foundation of their practice.

Those who have taken it up and incorporated it into their practice have participated in a development of the theory, subtly extending its implications: the miasm theory now involves far more than it did for Hahnemann. The first shift in meaning came with Hahnemann himself, in whose use of the term we can already see the beginning of an extension from the simple 'infectious disease' to the more complex 'consequences of the suppression of infectious disease'. Later there seems to have been another shift, whereby the term 'miasm' was used to refer not only to an infectious disease, and the consequence of the suppression of such disease, but also to the possibility that such chronic disease patterns might be inherited.

It is difficult to be absolutely clear from Hahnemann's description of the miasms whether he himself thought they could be inherited. It would have been hard for him to have formulated such a theory in precise terms, since theories of heredity such as we now take for granted were then in their infancy.[8] Hahnemann did, however, write of psora having existed for thousands of years and, in the sixth edition of the *Organon*, added the notion of inheritance to the text of the comment he wrote there about miasms.[9] This shift in his thinking seems to have taken place over the last years of his life, or perhaps he was merely making explicit what had been implicit earlier.[10] It is this aspect of the theory, however, which has dominated the development of miasmatic theory in the years since his death, because the concept of miasms has been incorporated into the homeopathic theory of constitution.

Further expansion of Hahnemann's original idea has come about through the writings of those who have developed theories concerning miasms other than psora. Originally Hahnemann said that he thought psora was responsible for seven-eighths of human disease, and the venereal miasms, syphilis and sycosis, for the other eighth. It was Henry Allen and other homeopaths in America who expanded Hahnemann's thinking in this area, and in so doing took the idea of miasms right away from Hahnemann's original notion that chronic disease was caused by a physical infection and the consequences of its suppression, thus introducing a moralistic element. Miasms, said these influential Swedenborgians, were caused by man's sin: psora represented the state of separation from God.[11] In the years since then there have been other, less moralistic, developments. These mainly seek to suggest that other diseases and also the effects of drugs may be considered to be the basis of chronic disease – that they may, in other words, be miasmatic.

In the course of its more recent development, or restatements, the theory seems to have come to resemble the old idea of a diathesis or disposition to disease.[12] Many homeopaths now consider that the term miasm may apply to any disease, whether infectious or not, which has the capacity to remain latent in the organism or system and manifest in different forms at different times. This, in its most modern form, would account for the slow viruses of contemporary medicine. In modern parlance a miasm now seems to mean a tendency to chronic disease initiated by the acquired or inherited effects of psora, of venereal disease, of tuberculosis or cancer, or even of less apparently noxious diseases such as influenza. The term has been extended far beyond Hahnemann's use of it.[13]

ACUTE DISEASE

Although Hahnemann's practice was concerned mostly with the treatment of chronic disease, acute diseases occasionally reached him for treatment and his patients frequently report having suffered from them in the past. Acute fevers of various kinds were common occurrences in Hahnemann's patients. and it is apparent from a glance at any contemporary materia medica that the phenomenon of fever was very important in the days when homeopathy first took root. The symptoms are highly developed and differentiated in most remedies; Hahnemann wrote extensively on the subject[14] and Boenninghausen produced a repertory devoted entirely to fever.[15]

There were many kinds of fever active in the early nineteenth century, not always as clearly distinguished as they are now but having in common high temperature, loss of fluids, weakness and, all too often, death. Common were the ague, puerperal fever, intermittent fevers of various kinds, bilious fever, typhus fever, putrid fever, catarrhal fever. Hahnemann occasionally specified some of these conditions by name when he encountered them in his patients, even though he was not concerned to differentiate them in this way. Nevertheless, fevers of various kinds were reported often, even in what was substantially a chronic practice outside of a hospital environment. Malaria, yellow fever and typhus or typhoid (not distinguished at the time) were sometimes reported by those who had travelled abroad.

Measles, scarlatina, whooping cough and smallpox were commonly reported. Smallpox was not such a threat in Hahnemann's day as it had been in previous generations. Though many had suffered and died from it, normally in childhood, even more had benefited from methods of inoculation against it, first introduced into Europe from Turkey at the beginning of the eighteenth century by the intrepid Lady Wortley Montagu. Hahnemann himself remarked that 'the widespread use of vaccination has so effectively put an end to all epidemics of the terribly deadly smallpox that the present generation no longer has any clear idea of this hideous bygone scourge.'[16] As yet he had observed only the temporary ill effects of vaccination in some patients who had been vaccinated by the old method (via the arm), and who had persistent problems with localised swellings. It remained for other homeopaths to notice that vaccination itself frequently created the conditions for chronic disease.

However, the predominant acute miasm affecting the population which provided Hahnemann's patients was, in addition to these common ordinary transient fevers, cholera. Although many died of it, many also survived and we see them still suffering from the after-effects of the disease. The Hahnemanns arrived in Paris only three years after the first great outbreak in Europe of the cholera which had broken out in Asia in the second quarter of the nineteenth century and made its slow but inexorable progression along the trade routes.[17] By 1831 it had reached Russia, then swiftly spread to Prussia and Austria. It swept through France and especially Paris with devastating effect. In the French capital the epidemic lasted for six months and six days and doubled the normal rate of mortality, which was already high. It caused enormous fear, because the process by which it spread was not understood. There were fierce arguments as to whether it was caused by contagion, epidemic constitution or local miasms. Those who were able to do so fled Paris, while the rest of the population refused to leave the assumed protection of their houses. Melanie's father had himself been affected, but had recovered.

Although some of Hahnemann's practice was concerned with the treatment of acute diseases in their active state, it was largely concerned with treating the lasting effects of such illnesses and their treatments. These originally acute illnesses had frequently been transformed into chronic illnesses in Hahnemann's patients, either because of allopathic treatment or because the patient had imperfectly recovered. It might even be appropriate to speak of the existence of a cholera miasm operating in Paris at this time (in the modern sense of the term). Several of his patients report that they have never been well since having the cholera in 1832: Mme Camus, M. Cuyala, Dr Deleau, M. Hubert, Mme Leloir, Mme Rapin and Dr Quin were among these.

THE PRESCRIBING OF SULPHUR

Hahnemann's main interest and preoccupation was with the chronic disease presented to him by most of his patients. The logical consequence of his theory of psora was that he began to prescribe the chief antipsoric remedy, Sulphur, to an extraordinary degree. Since everyone was psoric, he seems to have decided, everyone should benefit from Sulphur. Whereas in the earlier years of his practice he had prescribed on the basis of what he had termed a 'totality' of individual and characteristic symptoms, he now took to opening the majority of his chronic cases with Sulphur, thereby choosing to override what at one time he might have considered to be important characteristic symptoms, in order, presumably, to begin the case by prescribing for the underlying psoric miasm.

So, for instance, when Mr Campbell consulted him about an eruption on his face, caused by his having been treated for 'chancre' with allopathic medicines, Hahnemann opened the case with Sulphur, only following up with the 'syphilitic' remedy Cinnabar after clearing some of the case with the Sulphur.

Author's Note: Passages in italics in the case given below, and in subsequent cases in this book, are in Hahnemann's handwriting in the original casebooks. Melanie's entries are in plain type.

Mr Campbell (See facsimile, overleaf) was a 27-year-old Scotsman staying in the Hotel Bristol on the Place Vendôme. He first came to see Hahnemann on February 3rd 1840. Hahnemann wrote that he had had a chancre eighteen months earlier. He had been given a lot of allopathic medicine and after a few weeks his whole body was covered with pustules, especially his scalp and beard. His hair fell out. At the same time he developed mouth ulcers and was prescribed a potassium water. He took this for three months without change; he consulted Dr Quin in England and was treated and pronounced cured.

He then got a new chancre and while waiting for an appointment with Hahnemann, who had a cold, he took some mercury and applied an ointment to the chancre for twelve days and it vanished. He also took some sarsaparilla. Hahnemann wrote:

Now he has syphilitic spots which change size and there are especially big ones on his back. He has no more mouth ulcers. He is constipated when he doesn't walk a lot. He often suffers from vertigo, especially in his room. He cannot work here – even noise from the street disturbs him. He has nocturnal pollutions every 15 days. The spots on his forehead are made worse by his hat.

Prescription
Sulphur 190c (. /190), 1 drop to be diluted in 8 tablespoonfuls [of water and] ¹/₂ of alcohol, 1 tablespoonful to be [taken from this and] put in a glass [of water], 1–3 [teaspoonfuls] to be taken from this [daily].

February 10th [1840]
He's had no more vertigo. He has not been irritated by the noise from the street. Before coming to see me he drank tea twice a day but he has stopped. He has had one stool each day. He has had some enjoyable walks. He has the same venereal spots on the forehead which are not painful except when pressed.

Prescription
Sulphur (crossed out) *then Cinnabar 30c, (. /X) 1 drop to be diluted in 15 tablespoonfuls of water and 1 of alcohol. 1 tablespoonful to be taken from this and put in a glass of water, 1–2 [teaspoonfuls] to be taken [daily].*

He followed the Cinnabar 30c with a further prescription of Cinnabar 24c, then repeated Sulphur 190c before giving Merc. Sol. 30c, achieving a marked improvement in Mr Campbell's health before his patient returned to Scotland.

Hahnemann's prescriptions are rarely written out in full. The entries in this case are among the fullest. However, the pattern is sufficiently clear to provide a reasonable degree of certainty in expanding abbreviations. Usually he prescribed his remedies in one or more drops of the liquid potency, written . or .. or ... according to how many drops were to be used. These drops were added to a variable number of spoonfuls of water and alcohol. The spoons were described as: tablespoon (c a b = cuillère à bouche), teaspoon (pet c) or coffeespoon (c a cafe), or else simply as a spoonful (c = cuillerée), which I have normally assumed to be a tablespoonful. Where the size of the dose or spoon is not indicated in any way, I have enclosed my guess, here and in all subsequent cases, in square brackets.

Mr Campbell (27)   Hotel Bristol place Vendome

3 febr. avant 18 mois un chancre, on lui a donné qq m[édecine] qu'on a fait se retire pas de $ que en pharmacie que d'une pareille chancre
a peû 4 q semaines il fut ranger de bouton, sur tout le corps
mais surtout au visage — chercher (les cheveux tombent)

à la barbe.
cela a été Nov. et Dec. de 1838
au même tems des ulcéres à la bouche
alors $ et potasse (biod. potahique?)
puis cette $ et cette eau de potasse, qq. d' 3 mois sans changement
mais $ le 1 Mai, il fut un an de France de Qui après de qui il fut 6 semai,
repris à celui — quelques mois avant tu s'épt. il manifesta Qui
sur til se trouve bien — qu'in le prononça guéri,

1 Oct. il fut chez m^r. pour un nouveau chancre je lai' difforé pour
3 jours par mon rhume — en Eng$e il peut un $ d'un en oriént
appliqué un chancre 12 jours quil fut enncouè
puis de la sarsaparille

Ha maintenant des taches de Syphilis. Et qui changent
Se rogrofeur, dans des so plus grandes encore,
Pes plus qq apithès dans la bouche.
quand il ne ce promene trop il est constipé!
+ il souffre souvent de vertige, surtout à la chambre
alors il ne peut rien travailler, le travail le commode

42

Mr Campbell: Entirely in Hahnemann's hand. Note his (regular) use of the sigil symbol for Sulphur. Two different scales of potency are shown (see Chapters 8 and 9). Prescriptions make use of characteristic abbreviations, including a (smudged) sigil for sac lac at the foot of the page.

He adopted similar tactics when Mme Camus came, suffering not only from grief arising from the death of two of her children, but also from bowel disturbances which she had been experiencing since having had cholera seven years earlier. Despite such an important mental symptom and a clear 'exciting cause', Hahnemann opened treatment with Sulphur and continued to repeat it daily, interspersed with sac lac, until his patient improved considerably. (It is important to remember that at this period Hahnemann prescribed all his remedies in liquid potencies repeated daily or more often.)[18] He only twice gave her other remedies: once Ignatia, when she reported that she had developed diarrhoea from chagrin, and once, towards the end of her treatment, Nux Moschata.

When Mlle Sheila Brugmann was brought to him in a state of near mania, Hahnemann prescribed Sulphur and sac lac at first, before turning to remedies seemingly more specifically related to her behaviour and condition: remedies such as Laurocerasus, Nux Moschata, Phosphorus, Platina, Stramonium and Hyoscyamus. He followed a similar procedure with Mme de Champagny of Bordeaux, who had contracted a venereal disease from her husband sixteen years previously and was still suffering its effects, despite having received various kinds of allopathic treatment. In particular she suffered from attacks of night agitation and deafness. Hahnemann, however, ignored the apparently current symptoms and treated her with repeated doses of Sulphur and sac lac until she also was much improved.

From the earliest days of the Paris practice it was common for Hahnemann to prescribe Sulphur at the outset of a case, and to continue to do so until other symptoms more characteristic of other remedies manifested themselves. It appears to have been Hahnemann's practice then to prescribe on the basis of these new symptoms, until these symptoms improved, or until fresh symptoms characteristic of another remedy emerged, or until symptoms markedly characteristic of Sulphur itself began to reappear. Hahnemann thus seems to have seen Sulphur, with its vast field of symptoms reflecting the psoric state of humanity, as a sort of bass remedy to which others were the melody. He always returned to it when in doubt, or when the progress of the case was slow or stuck.

For example, Mme Laplace came complaining of difficulty with her periods: she was experiencing a great deal of pain and was vomiting up to twenty-five times a day. Hahnemann began the prescribing with Sulphur. After a few prescriptions her periods improved, but she became feverish and was therefore prescribed Aconite, followed by Nux Vomica when constipation ensued upon the fever. He reverted to Sulphur when the fever and constipation had passed. In Mme Leloir's case (pages 54 *seq.*), Hahnemann opened with successive prescriptions of Sulphur, repeated daily until the marked characteristic symptom of 'wind' appeared, whereupon he prescribed Lycopodium with the intention (indicated in the margin) of returning to Sulphur when the wind had abated. However, when Mme Leloir developed pains in the kidneys after taking the Lycopodium, he prescribed Rhus Tox. until these symptoms subsided, leaving only the symptoms of pain in the stomach, wind and itching in the ears which he controlled successfully with Hepar Sulph. Only much later did he return to prescribing Sulphur.

In the later stages of his practice Hahnemann frequently prescribed Sulphur alone for long periods of time, sometimes completing whole cases without resorting to any other remedies, even when clear indications for them could be seen. This method seems to have been as successful in achieving cure as any more individualising way of prescribing.

For instance, M. Persin came in 1839, suffering from pain in the urethral canal consequent upon venereal disease. He had had more than twenty recurrences of a discharge since he had first contracted gonorrhoea at the age of seventeen. Sulphur interspersed with sac lac was used for a long time in preference to apparently better indicated gonorrhoeal remedies, such as Thuja, which in earlier days Hahnemann had been quick to use in cases of this kind. In 1840 the sculptor David d'Angers had his arthritis controlled with Sulphur and sac lac, while in 1841 the cellist Max Böhrer was freed of cramps in the fingers of his bowing hand with this single remedy. Mme Moreau came in June 1841, suffering from the long-standing effects of smallpox vaccination and of numerous medications including mercury, as a result of which she had lost all her teeth. Hahnemann treated her uninterruptedly (and successfully) with Sulphur and sac lac for several months (see pages 47–53).

Despite the theoretical support for an initial prescription of Sulphur in every case, there were several situations in which Hahnemann did not begin treatment with the antipsoric. When a patient came for a first consultation in an acute phase of illness, he normally prescribed for the acute state first.

For example, when M. Barré, the umbrella-maker, came for his first consultation the day after a major attack of epilepsy, still suffering from smaller convulsive attacks in its wake, Hahnemann treated him with Valerian every two hours for two days during the acute attacks, then with Cuprum every two hours. When these attacks had subsided he began to treat the underlying case with Sulphur, followed by a series of remedies in response to the emerging symptom picture, and finally with Sulphur again for some weeks. He succeeded in completely eliminating the problem: when M. Barré returned a year later with another complaint, he reported that he had had no further incidence of epilepsy. When Mme Rougier came with lancinating pains around the heart and continuous palpitations, Hahnemann prescribed Causticum every hour in the first instance, followed by Pulsatilla and Valerian and only went on to Sulphur when this condition had improved a little. When M. Dupart came for treatment in the middle of a gonorrhoeal discharge, Hahnemann gave him Cannabis immediately. Only when the acute symptoms had subsided did he begin to treat the underlying case with Sulphur. When M. Voisin de Gartempe consulted him, speaking darkly of domestic vexations, perpetual anxiety, melancholy, discontent with himself and thoughts of suicide, Hahnemann gave him Staphysagria immediately and, when it did not help, went on quickly to Aurum.

We can see that by the time he came to Paris Hahnemann had considerably simplified his method of remedy selection. This was mainly because his ideas about the simillimum had changed a great deal since the days when he intended it to cover the totality of the visible symptoms of the patient. Now, with a whole new theory of chronic disease behind him, he was determined to deal with the invisible symptoms too.

It is in the method of choosing the remedy for the patient that these casebooks manifest some of the most important discrepancies between the received information about Hahnemann's prescribing and the actual facts. Whatever Hahnemann might have thought and written in his early life, it is clear that in his later days he became a miasmatic prescriber. His clear intention was to treat the psoric miasm before beginning any other treatment of more individual symptoms.

Name: MOREAU Emile, Mme
Age: 34, married

Casebook entries: **13**/61–62 (see facsimile, overleaf)

June 12th [1841]
(Menses 27th May.)
She has had no pain since she was 15.
At the age of 25 she was vaccinated for the second time [with material] taken from a child covered with spots and since then she has had spots on her face.
A mercurial ointment has been applied. Eight leeches have been applied to her thighs three times a year.
This April 15 leeches were applied, without effect.
Her menses last for only 24 hours . . . for 15 years, since her marriage.
At the age of 26 she lost her teeth.
She gets red marks and spots on her cheek-bones when she works and also in various other unremarkable situations.
She only drinks water, not coffee or tea. She is not to drink beer.
She has no pain with her menses.
She takes enemas and baths too frequently.
She sleeps well.

Prescription
Sulphur LM 7 (7/o) in 7 [tablespoonfuls of water]and 1/2 [of alcohol decanted into] 2 glasses. Take 1 teaspoonful [daily].

June 18th [1841]
She has a coated tongue in the morning.
Her saliva, she says, has ruined not only her own teeth, but also those she had been given.
She never blows her nose except when she has a cold.
She eats sweets all day.

Prescription
Sulphur LM 8 (. /8/o).

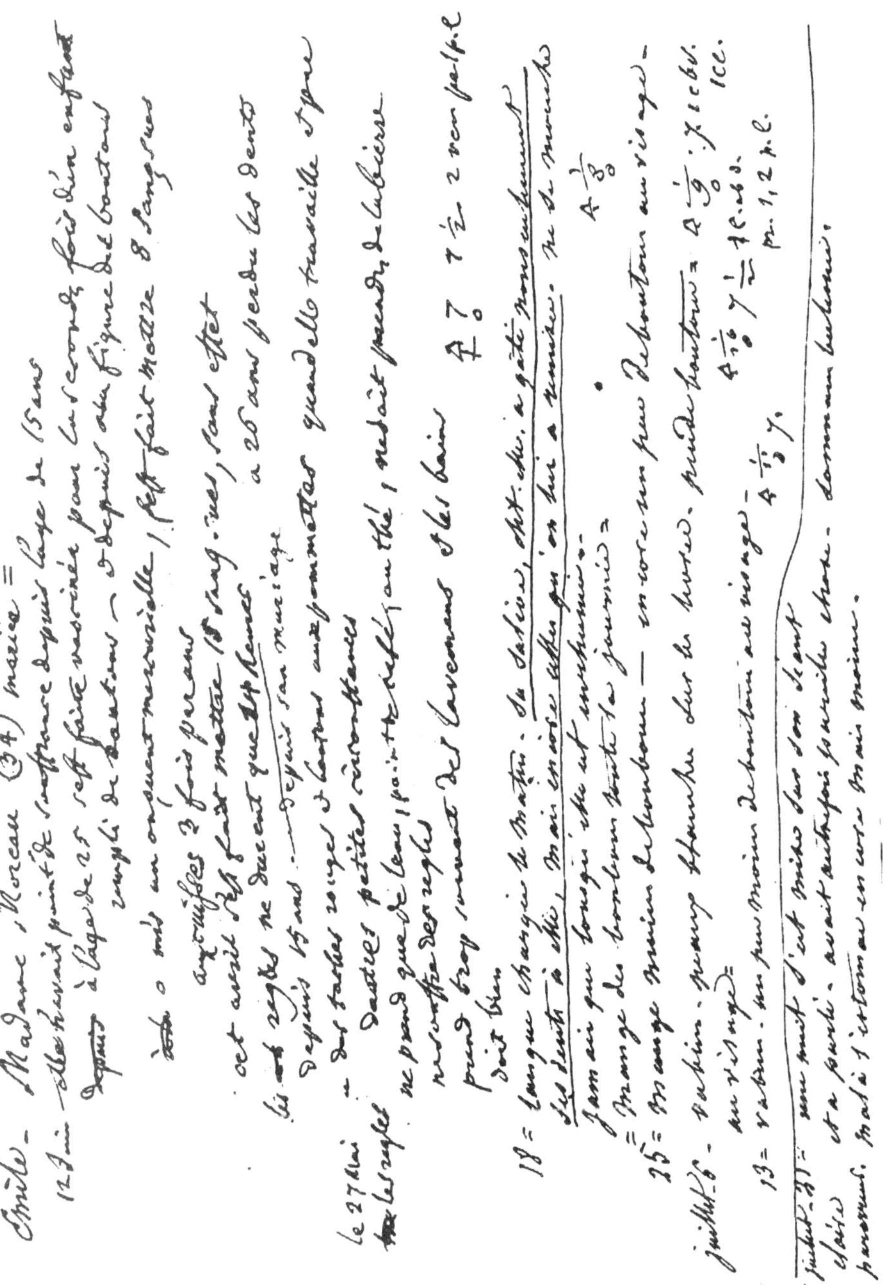

Mme Moreau: Written by both Samuel (first hand) and Melanie (second hand). There is the introduction of notes on the patient's daughter Claire into text on Mme Moreau (not an uncommon practice when seeing different family members). Note the o = globule sign for LM potency, very abbreviated prescriptions and clear use of the sac lac sigil. Note also the use of $, apparently as a symbol for sac lac. Elsewhere a similar symbol is clearly not intended to represent sac lac but acts as some kind of marker for the beginning of a prescription (see Leloir extract, pages 56–7).

June 25th [1841]
She's eating fewer sweets, still has a few spots on her face.

Prescription
Sulphur – LM 9 (. /9/o) in seven [tablespoonsful of water and alcohol].
One tablespoonful in a glass of water and one coffeespoonful from
that.

July 6th [1841]
She's doing well. White spots on her lips. She has few spots on her
face.

Prescription
Sulphur LM 10 (. /10/o) in 7 [tablespoonsful of water] and 1/2 [of
alcohol]. Take 1 tablespoonful from this and 1–2 teaspoons [daily]
from that.

July 13th [1841]
Doing well. A little fewer spots on the face.

Prescription
Sulphur LM 11 (. /11/o) in 7 [tablespoonsful].

July 21st [1841]
(Claire – included here by mistake)
One night she sat straight up in bed and talked. Similar things have
happened on other occasions: somnambulism.
Had stomach pain again, but less.

Prescription
Sac lac in 8 for Madame.
(To Léonie sac lac)

July 28th [1841]
(*Menses 14th July.*)
Fewer pustules on the face. For the rest she is very well.

Prescription
Sulphur LM 11 (. /11/o) in 7 [tablespoonsful].

August 4th [1841]
She has spots on her forehead with little white heads (for nine years).
The skin on her lips is renewing itself (the lips are peeling).

Prescription
Sac lac in 7 [tablespoonsful].

August 11th [1841]
She has had a little aphthous ulcer in her mouth. She has had a great many spots coming and going on her forehead.

Prescription
Sulphur LM 12 (. /12/o).

August 18th [1841]
No more aphthous ulcers in her mouth, an itchy spot on her cheek-bone.

Prescription
Sac lac in 7 [tablespoonsful of water] and 1/2 [of alcohol].

August 25th [1841]
Her lips are peeling and the skin on her forehead has become smooth. When she leaves the white heads of the spots alone they do not itch. *But the little spots itch.*

Prescription
Sulphur LM 13 (. /13/o).

September 1st [1841]
(Claire – included here by mistake)
On the 28th and 29th she had more stomach pains, was a little constipated for two days; she often has pain in the middle of her back when she plays the piano or when she goes donkey-riding. She still has some pleasurable sensations in her womb.

Prescription
Sac lac.

September 1st [1841]
Madame Moreau
(Menses August 14th.)
A little agitated. Lips a little swollen. Fewer spots than usual.
Internal pulsations.

Prescription
Sac lac.

September 15th [1841]
Still spots.

Prescription
Sulphur LM 14 (. /14/o).

September 22nd [1841]
Fewer spots: for the rest she is well.

Casebook entry:
13/64

September 29th [1841]
Fewer spots.

Prescription
Sac lac.

October 6th [1841]
Fewer spots. A little blood to the head.

October 13th [1841]
A little cold in the head with sweating.

October 20th [1841]
A few spots on the forehead; the rest very good.
Very slightly swollen glands in the left breast.

Prescription
Sac lac.

October 29th [1841]
The skin of her lips is very dry, she has very few spots on her face.
A very slightly swollen gland in her breast – without pain.

Prescription
Sulphur LM 15 (. /15/o) in 15 [table]spoonfuls of water; take 1 [tea]spoonful [daily].

November 19th [1841]
Her lips are much dryer. Her skin is dry and thickened.
She has a few spots.

Prescription
Sulphur LM 16 (. /16/o) in 15 [table]spoonsful.

November 20th [1841]
No longer has spots on her face. Her lips are still dry.

Prescription
Sac lac.

November 27th [1841]
A little headache this evening. She has only taken one coffeespoonful of sac lac.

December 10th [1841]
Spots on the face are doing well.
A little lancinating pain in the small breast gland.

Prescription
Sulphur LM 17 (./17/o) in 15.

December 24th [1841]
She is doing well.

Prescription
Continue Sulphur LM 17 (. /17/o)

Name: LELOIR, Mme
Age 40, married, 2 children
Address: Rue Soeur de Madame 26

Casebook entry: **2**/191 (see facsimile, pages 56–7)

Mme Leloir first came in February 1836, suffering mainly from almost permanent wind, belching and stomach pains. She also had migraine, especially around the time of menstruation, and her periods had been disturbed for over a year – early, heavy and clotted. Hahnemann's first prescription was Sulphur 30c (. . /X), 2 drops in 15 tablespoonfuls. Mme Leloir returned later.

March 11th [1836]
Period March 6th. The last day was February 10th. (A lot of blood for 3 days and then a slight amount for eight days. The blood was clotted.)

She had the wind without the pain; she did not have attacks in the same way but during the night she felt pain in her stomach: it was not so strong. She's generally better. She can't have a stool without an enema. She has more appetite.

When she had the first spoonful of Sulphur she felt a tingling all over her skin. Leucorrhoea just as bad. Itching in the genital parts before the period. She is restless at the beginning of the night then she becomes calm and sleeps well. She has had itching in both ears for six months. Migraine during the period without nausea. She has a little cough without expectoration.

Prescription
Sulphur 24c (. . /VIII), 2 drops in 15 [table]spoonfuls.

April 6th [1836]
She hasn't noticed any change. She had three little attacks in the stomach each lasting about three minutes, they passed when she belched.

Periods 6th March (=27) and 1st April (=26). In the past she has had migraine a few days before her period but the last one was on the day immediately before the period and it was less severe. The blood was a lot less clotted, there was about half as much. Feet still cold.

When she goes to bed she still feels breathless until she belches and then she can sleep. No more itching in the genital parts. No more restlessness after going to bed. She was constipated for three days until she had an enema. She rarely has a stool unaided and then the stool is hard and passed with difficulty. Coughing much less, spitting a little in the mornings. She's eating very well. Always a lot of painless eructations. Still has the itching in both ears.

Prescription
[No. 1:] Lycopodium 30c (. /X), 1 drop in 15 [table]spoonfuls;
No. 2: Lycopodium 30c (. /X);
No. 3: in 15 [table]spoonfuls.
(Sulphur next.)

April 10th [1836]
She has pains in her kidneys: she's stiff and tired. This came on after the end of the period. The pain extends to her abdomen, which is sensitive to touch. She suffers more in the night than in the day. Everything else is just as usual. Always constipated. The pain which she feels in the kidneys seems better than before. Little wind now.
Has had no further itching in the genital parts.

Prescription
Rhus Tox. 30c (. /X), 1 drop in 7 [table]spoonfuls

Casebook entry: page 2/192 (see facsimile, pages 58–9)

April 11th [1836]
... three weeks ago some little red spots appeared at the place on her side where she now feels the most acute pain. Her belly was a little swollen and she had a few colicky pains which went after she achieved a motion with two enemas. After this indisposition the wind was much stronger and more frequent. In general she thinks she is more constipated since she has been having homeopathic treatment and the enemas are not so effective.

Prescription
Continue Tox.

Mme Leloir: Written by both Melanie (first hand) and Samuel (second hand). Note the use of R at the beginning of the prescription, and the $ sign in front of Rhus Tox. Elsewhere these symbols can represent inhale (respirer) and sac respectively, but here do not seem to have that meaning. Note Samuel's hand at the end of the first entry where he seems to have asked further questions and made a marginal note of likely remedies. Note also the apparently multiple prescription made on April 6th.

Mme Leloir: Date and duration of menses given in the margin – it was their normal practice to record this detail at every appointment. Note the citation of German repertory on page 59, lines 7–8. Also, the recapitulation of remedies already given, line 9. This case is studied further on pages 103–8.

May 26th [1836]

April 26th periods (= 24). Less heavy. On April 29th she had an eruption which resembled erysipelas. Her face was swollen. She had numerous little pointed spots which itched and smarted: her face was burning. She felt very well in herself during the eruption. When it was over her face was very white and pasty.

For 3 days from May 8th she had a migraine accompanied by stomach pains. The pains were bearable till the sixteenth and since then they have increased. Now she has pains in her stomach when she has eaten (also when she has not but they are not so strong then). When the pain is not so strong she feels hungry. When she belches her hunger is appeased.

Period May 20th (= 24 days). She is short of breath when she is in pain. Period only lasted two days instead of four or five.

Itching in the ears.

Excessive constipation. She can't go.

She had these pains first at the time of the cholera epidemic.

Author's Note: In the following and all subsequent repertorisations these are prefixed with either (G) or (F) to indicate that they were originally written in German or French.

Repertory

(G) *Stomach ulcer: Cann, Magn m, Rut, Stann., Coff, Hell, Natr m*

(G) *Wind: Ang; Bar; Chin, Colch, Con, Mos, Sabad., Alum, Mang, Ran sc.*

She has had Tox, Lyc, Lyc, Sulphur . . /VIII, Sulphur . . /X

Prescription

Hepar Sulph. 24c (. /VIII), 1 drop in 15 tablespoonfuls, take 1 tablespoonful daily.

June 13th [1836]

Her ears still itch but not so badly. She has had 2 stools naturally, which has not happened for a long time. Eructations without taste, more in the night than in the day. Teeth are decayed; she has attacks of toothache . . . She no longer has any pain in her stomach. Considerable leucorrhoea – without itching. She is losing less blood during her periods. . . . and she has no clotting any more. She has had two migraines but less severe. She is eating well. She no longer has the continual need to eat.

Prescription
Hepar Sulph. 18c (. /VI), 1 drop in 15 [table]spoonfuls.

NOTES

1. See S. Hahnemann, *Die chronischen Krankheiten*, Dresden and Leipzig 1835–9, *passim*.
2. S. Hahnemann, *Organon*, 6th edn, paragraph 72.
3. S. Hahnemann, *Organon*, 6th edn, paragraph 72.
4. The *Oxford English Dictionary* defines the early nineteenth-century use of the word miasm as follows: 'Infectious or noxious exhalations from putrescent organic matter; poisonous particles or germs floating in and polluting the atmosphere; noxious emanations, especially Malaria.' It cites an 1827 usage: 'It has long been familiar to physicians that there was produced by ... marshes and swamps, a poisonous and aeriform substance, the cause, not only of ordinary fevers, but of intermittents; and to this unknown agent of disease the term marsh miasma has been applied.'

Parr's *London Medical Dictionary* of 1809 is more detailed: 'Miasmata ... are the causes of some of the most fatal fevers to which mankind are subject. In the more strict pathological investigations of modern authors they are distinguished from contagion, which is confined to the effluvia from the human body, when subject to disease; yet this contagion, when it does not proceed immediately from the body, but has been for some time confined in clothes, is sometimes styled miasma. Miasma strictly speaking is an aerial fluid combined with atmospheric air, and not dangerous except the air be loaded with it. Each infectious disease has its own diffused round the person which it has attacked, and liable to convey the disease at different distances. A patient in the smallpox seems to diffuse an infectious atmosphere to the distance of from ten to fourteen feet, measles and scarlatina are less active in this respect, and even the plague seems not to be infectious ...'
5. S. Hahnemann, 'On the Mode of Propagation of the Asiatic Cholera', in *The Lesser Writings of Samuel Hahnemann*, ed. R. E. Dudgeon, London 1852, p. 851.
6. Quoted from L. H. Tafel's English translation of Hahnemann's *Die chronischen Krankheiten*, published as L. H. Tafel, *The Chronic Diseases*, Philadelphia 1896, Vol. 1, pp. 32–3.
7. *ibid*, Vol 1, p. 41ff.

8. Theories of biological heredity had hardly been formulated as yet. Lamarck had begun to publish his theories relative to evolution in 1809 and 1815–22, and 'his view that characteristics acquired by individual experience can be inherited was popular politically, and educationally.' (R. L. Gregory, *The Oxford Companion to the Mind*, referenced under Lamarck.) Insofar as disease could be regarded as an acquired characteristic, then presumably it could have been imagined that it might be inherited. However, Gregor Mendel's work on inheritance was not published until 1866 and not really appreciated until 1900, while the extension of the idea of heredity from property to nature is not recorded by the *OED* until 1863: 'The property of organic beings in virtue of which offspring inherit the nature and characteristics of parents and ancestors generally; the tendency of like to beget like.'

9. In two notes added to the 6th edition of the *Organon*, but not present in the 5th edition, Hahnemann mentions the idea of inherited miasms. In a note to paragraph 78 he refers to the 'disease acquired by contagion or inheritance', and in a note to paragraph 284 he remarks that 'it is usually through the milk of the nurse that most infants contract psora, if they have not already inherited it from the mother.'

10. In 1835 Melanie wrote a letter to Hahnemann in which she described her mother's emotional instability as being due to 'inherited psora'. This suggests that an extension of Lamarck's views already had some currency.

11. See further J. Henry Allen, *The Chronic Miasms*, Chicago and James Tyler Kent, *Lectures on Homeopathic Philosophy*, Lancaster, Pennsylvania 1900. Many of the early American homeopaths were followers of Swedenborg and sought to bring homeopathy fully into sympathy with some of the tenets of his church.

12. The word 'diathesis' is Greek for a disposition or state. *OED* gives its medical use as: 'A permanent (hereditary or acquired) condition of the body which renders it liable to certain special diseases or affections; a constitutional predisposition or tendency.' The concept of diathesis was current in orthodox medicine in Hahnemann's day.

13. Such an extension of meaning as has been implied by modern homeopaths is, of course, difficult to support in terms of modern scientific understanding of genetics. However, theories of morphic resonance, such as those proposed by Rupert Sheldrake, may provide some answers to this problem in the future. See R. Sheldrake, *The Presence of the Past*, Collins, London 1988.

14. S. Hahnemann, *Organon*, 6th edn, paragraph 73 and R. E. Dudgeon ed., *The Lesser Writings of Samuel Hahnemann*, London 1852, *passim*.

15. C. von Boenninghausen, *Versuch einer homöopathischen Therapie der Wechselfieber*, Münster 1833.

16. S. Hahnemann, *Organon*, 6th edn, paragraph 56.

Long before Jenner's experiments with cowpox, people had protected themselves against the ravages of smallpox by introducing a small amount of diseased pus from a smallpox victim's arm into the arm of a healthy person, in order to contract what they hoped would be a milder form of the disease. However, the attack of smallpox resulting from this inoculation was not always a mild one and was fatal in two or three cases out of a hundred. Though by the end of the eighteenth century the inoculation had been refined to the transfer of a drop of pus by a lancet into a small pinprick, Jenner's development of the cowpox vaccine in 1796 was preferred because it was assumed to be less dangerous.

See further H. J. Parish, *A History of Immunization*, London 1965; H. J. Parish and D. A. Cannon, *Antisera, Toxins, Vaccines and Tuberculins*, London 1962; G. Miller, *The Adoption of Inoculation for Smallpox in England and France*, Pennsylvania 1957.

17. For details of this devastating epidemic, see R. and J. Dubos, *The White Plague*, London 1953; M. Durey, *The Return of the Plague*, Ireland 1979; N. Longmate, *King Cholera: The Biography of a Disease*, London 1966; F. H. F. Quin, *Du traitement homéopathique du choléra*, Paris 1832.

18. For fuller details about potencies and prescribing see Chapters 8 and 9.

Chapter 4

Choosing the Remedy to Follow Sulphur

Once he had treated the psoric miasm and exhausted the action of Sulphur, how then did Hahnemann proceed to select his other remedies? It will already be clear that he was not as doctrinaire in his practical prescribing as his theoretical writings might lead us to expect – it is therefore difficult to characterise completely his method of choosing the remedy. What needs to be emphasised throughout is his pragmatism and experimentalism: he was learning about his new medicine and he was willing to try anything in pursuit of knowledge. However, he had already made a number of discoveries and observations about homeopathy and the use of its remedies, and he did not fling these away after developing the miasm theory; rather, he sought to incorporate his old observations into his new theory.

CHARACTERISTIC SYMPTOMS

After the first action of Sulphur had been exhausted he selected the subsequent remedies according to a number of criteria, all of which he had employed in previous years. Chief of these, according to the *Organon*, was that the prescribing symptoms should be characteristic or distinctive; it is clear that Hahnemann used this criterion wherever possible, selecting characteristic (or at least prominent) symptoms which emerged in the patient's picture after Sulphur had acted for a while. For instance, he gave Cicuta Virosa to Mme Braun because she had a 'craving for the taste of charcoal', Agaricus to Lord Capel because of his persistently 'twitching eyelids', Aurum to Mme Peigne when she told him of her 'desire to commit suicide', Sabadilla to Miss Stirling who was having 'dark thoughts', Lycopodium to M. Voisin de Gartempe because of his 'desire to be alone', Ambra Grisea to M. Musard because of 'voluptuous itching of the scrotum', Causticum to M. Musard because of a persistent sore throat with a 'grazed sensation', Conium to Mme Leloir when she told him of her 'involuntary swallowing worse walking in wind' and Staphysagria to Master Kalkbrenner when told of the (undefined) 'effects of masturbation'. The use of such symptoms as a basis for choosing a remedy was usual for Hahnemann.

If no particularly characteristic symptoms were present, Hahnemann would then select his remedy on the basis of any important or prominent symptoms. If these were not present, he seems to have been satisfied to prescribe on the basis of any persisting physical symptoms, even if they were quite common – he prescribed Plumbum or Opium on no other indication than 'constipation', for instance. He clearly had a range of remedies which he 'thought of' in certain pathological states. In the ensuing chapters it will be clear that Hahnemann quite often effectively prescribed in terms of what we now call 'therapeutics': there were, for instance, rheumatic remedies, paralytic remedies, respiratory remedies, urinary remedies.[1]

REPERTORIES

Hahnemann's selection of remedies was often supported by the use of repertories: rubrics are frequently cited in the casebooks. Although Hahnemann's knowledge of remedies was very detailed, since he had personally proved many of those which he used most frequently, he also had access to several embryonic repertories. His own compilations of indices to symptoms, which exist in manuscript in the Institut für die Geschichte der Medizin, are not repertories in the modern sense: they do not combine several symptoms under one heading and list all associated remedies, but are more specifically alphabetical indices to the provings. His colleagues Baron Maria Clemens von Boenninghausen[2] and Dr Georg Jahr[3] had both produced more complex repertories, experimenting with various ways of categorising the symptoms of remedies. Hahnemann also cited a French repertory quite frequently towards the end of his time in Paris. I have, however, been unable to determine from which specific repertories he was actually drawing in the casebooks.

Hahnemann seems to have used repertories more as aids to memory than as a part of any method of case analysis, such as understood by modern homeopaths. Usually he noted only one or two rubrics, apparently using them to remind himself of the remedies indicated for certain key symptoms, either unusual, characteristic or persistent. Sometimes he prescribed one of the remedies indicated in a rubric or rubrics, in which case it is perfectly clear on what indications he was prescribing. Sometimes he prescribed a remedy in no way indicated in the chosen rubrics, in which case it is less clear. Frequently, having carefully repertorised for more specific remedies, he nevertheless prescribed Sulphur.[4]

Occasionally he gave a fuller explanation for the selection of the remedy than just one rubric: he gave China to Mme Lamarichale, as he wrote, because of 'desire to weep, soft stools and palpitations'. He gave Muriatic Acid to Mrs Lennox 'for deafness and the throat', and prescribed Bryonia to be inhaled by M. Laterade 'whenever he was annoyed'.

With the small number of remedies he had at his disposal, Hahnemann could rarely have hoped to achieve the grail of what we would now call an exact simillimum. Indeed, even now our vastly increased number of remedies is still not adequate to mirror exactly the myriad individual expressions of disease in the billions of the earth's population. He had to be content to move through the case, eliminating symptoms serially, following his principle that the symptoms were the illness and that if they were removed then so would the illness be. The symptoms were the expression of the vital force untuned. As he removed each symptom, so he tuned each note until eventually the whole instrument might be restored to harmony.

We might be surprised to realise how partial were the indications on which he was willing to prescribe, moving the case along by small steps. If the chosen remedy did not remove the symptom quickly, he selected another remedy having that same symptom. There is an extreme example of this in Mr Robert Lyster's case, where Hahnemann worked his way serially through all five remedies included in the rubric 'amaurosis': Spigelia, Guaiacum, Cinnabar, Ruta and Silica, until some improvement was eventually achieved with the last one.

Of course he often failed. There are no miraculous transformations in these casebooks. No one emerges from the Hahnemanns' consulting room a fully realised human being with all miasms cleared. People do often emerge, however, in better health, with fewer symptoms and less interference with their capacity to lead a healthy life. And this despite the fact that Hahnemann had to plough his way through thickly encrusted layers of disease miasm and the effects of allopathic treatment, before he could even touch the patient's own nature. And despite the fact that he was working with a very small number of remedies.

FREQUENT CHANGE OF REMEDY

Because he responded quickly to changes of symptoms, Hahnemann naturally changed remedies frequently. Gone now is the caution of the 1820s when he had urged his pupils to wait until the action of one remedy had ceased before prescribing another. There is less thought now of length of action of the remedy, but rather the recognition that by the old method cure was too slow. He was prepared, now, to risk exacerbation of the symptoms by repeating the remedy.[5] At this stage Hahnemann might respond to any kind of symptom, whether it were an aggravation from the remedy, a return of old symptoms, a symptom of the remedy or a new symptom of the patient, sometimes prescribing a fresh remedy, sometimes preferring to give sac lac. Later he became more patient and prescribed sac lac more often.

If the symptom aggravated, he sometimes saw the character of the aggravation as an indication for another active remedy, and might treat the symptoms emerging in the aggravation. M. Rousselot's symptoms aggravated after Nux Vomica, and Hahnemann immediately prescribed Hepar Sulph. to counter the aggravation. Mme Gueroult had an aggravation after Ambra Grisea and inhaled Camphor to counter it. When she aggravated on a high potency of Sulphur, having been symptom-free at lower potencies, she inhaled Coffea several times to antidote it. When Mme Grisenoi was aggravated by Belladonna, Hahnemann immediately prescribed Rhus Tox. Mrs Lewis was prescribed Platina, and when the pain in the polyps in her womb increased after this, she was first told to dilute the dose further and was then prescribed Teucrium Marum.

At other times, in such circumstances, Hahnemann preferred to prescribe sac lac until the aggravation settled down, and he did this increasingly as the years went by. Mme Maurice, who was known to be 'very susceptible to medicines', having already been treated by homeopaths in Lyon, was given sac lac for several days every time she had an aggravation. Mme Giffrier had 'a good deal of aggravation of the pains in her uterus' after a second prescription of Sulphur, but he gave simply sac lac for several days then sac lac interspersed with Sulphur. Similarly, he gave sac lac when Mme Dessiers had 'an unpleasant aggravation of genital itching' after Ammonium Carb. Mlle Badbedat had extremely itchy scabs: treated with Borax she produced new stomach symptoms and an aggravation of the skin condition. Hahnemann persisted in his use of Borax, interspersing it with sac lac, until the scabs began to improve. M. Lecointe's eye being much worse for Oxymuriatic Acid, he was tempted to give China and wrote this name in the margin, but eventually he gave sac lac till the aggravation subsided. He then continued with Phosphorus, followed by Isopath. M. Wartel was given Sulphur 30c when he had skin eruptions all over his body. He was much worse a week later and Hahnemann therefore prescribed Sulphur 24c first, up to nine doses daily and then Sulphur 24c and sac lac on alternate days, followed by Sulphur 18c and sac lac. After this his skin was much better.

If there was a return of old symptoms Hahnemann would sometimes prescribe for these, as in the case of Mme Carré, whose old symptoms returned after a prescription of Ranunculus Sceleratus: Graphites was prescribed in response. Spigelia brought back Charles French's gonorrhoeal discharge, which was then treated with Clematis. Mme de St. Cloud had a bad aggravation accompanied by a return of old symptoms after a dose of Sulphur. Hahnemann continued in this case to prescribe the Sulphur, but gave her some Nux Vomica which she was to take to cancel the Sulphur if she became very ill again. Later on, when she suffered greatly after a prescription of Kali Carb., Hahnemann again prescribed Nux Vomica until the symptoms were better. Mme Berthou had had pneumonia for two months and had been left with an internal right-sided pain, heaviness, tiredness, a painful spot and burning down to the sacrum on the right side, as well as vertigo which made her fearful and inclined to fall to the right. She also suffered from noises in the ears and head. Hahnemann began by prescribing one dose of Sulphur . / 190 (to take here) and Bryonia daily. Three minutes after the first dose of Bryonia she had pains in the stomach (Hahnemann wrote 'return of old symptoms'), green expectoration, spittle and pus. He responded to this with Staphysagria until she gradually improved. He then gave her sac lac for a while. (He often indicated his opinion that a symptom was an old one returning by noting 'ancien symptôme' in the margins of his casebook.)

Similarly, if new symptoms appeared they were sometimes noted: 'nouveau symptôme' and prescribed for. This did not happen as frequently as in the case of returned old symptoms. For instance, when Mme Maurice was generally much improved on Nux Moschata, Hahnemann noted the appearance of the new symptom of an increased desire for urination twice before eventually prescribing for it. When Mme de la Roche was given Hepar Sulph. and produced the new symptom of 'lancinating pains in the womb before periods', Hahnemann gave her Nux Moschata.

REMEDIES IN TANDEM OR ALTERNATION

This combination of frequent repetition of remedies, and frequent changing of remedies in response to the appearance of new symptoms, necessarily led quite commonly to situations in which Hahnemann could be found prescribing Sulphur and an apsoric remedy (or some-times even another antipsoric) in tandem. It is not usually completely clear from the casebooks whether and when the taking of Sulphur was suspended once the new remedy was introduced. Sometimes it clearly was suspended, as in the case of M. Musard (see page 171). Sometimes it is probable that it was not, as in the case of General Griois, who seems to have been given Thuja 30c once a day in the morning while still taking several liquid doses of Sulphur 192c daily. On the whole we may assume that the daily administration of Sulphur was usually suspended while the new remedy was used. However, even when it is clear that the administration of Sulphur had been suspended, the prescription of the second remedy seems to have been made within a time span which a modern homeopath (and Hahnemann himself in earlier days) might well regard as being within the duration of the action of Sulphur. The truth is that by now Hahnemann was not concerned to wait for the action of Sulphur to end – he was more interested in prescribing on the *results* of its action: characteristically he prescribed on symptoms given expression, as it were, by the Sulphur.

It appears to have been important to Hahnemann to prescribe Sulphur and the associated remedy, when taken in tandem or in alternation, in different potencies, at what we might now call different resonant frequencies. It was usual for him to prescribe Sulphur (or the bass remedy) in a higher potency than the subsidiary (or melodic) remedy, or else to instruct that one of them be inhaled rather than taken orally. So, for example, when M. de Simencourt came with his sight badly affected following a cerebral fever caused by a fall from a horse, Hahnemann treated him with Sulphur in a high centesimal potency and Arnica in a low centesimal potency in alternation, until his eyesight and other after-effects of the cerebral fever improved. M. Musard, while taking Sulphur orally daily in a centesimal potency was to inhale Nux Vomica and later Opium, when needed. Occasionally Sulphur was to be inhaled while the subsidiary remedy was administered orally. When Mme Chueleher consulted Hahnemann about her palpitations, she was told to inhale Sulphur in a high centesimal potency in the evenings and to take Aconite orally in a low centesimal potency in the mornings. It always seems to have been important to him to maintain this difference in frequency.

Alternation of remedies in the treatment of acute diseases was quite common, especially in the case of any feverish illness. In such cases the alternating remedies were usually prescribed in the same potency. So for example Mme de Chousy, who had been treated mainly with Sulphur daily for over two and a half months, succumbed to a fever caused by the sun: she was prescribed Arsenicum 30c for three days, followed by Ipecac. and Nux Vomica 30c on alternate days. When the fever recurred at a later phase of the treatment, Hahnemann immediately prescribed Ipecac. and Nux Vomica 30c in alternation, and followed this up with Arnica and Antimonium Crudum 30c in alternation.[6]

When reading Hahnemann's cases, it becomes ever more apparent that his advice in the *Organon* about selecting the simillimum on the basis of the totality of symptoms was, as such textbook instructions usually are, a counsel of perfection and not something he invariably did, or indeed was able to do in day-to-day practice. Patients simply do not always present with a clear 'totality of symptoms', or even with useful characteristic symptoms pointing straight to a single remedy. This is not in any way to criticise him for failing to be the perfect practitioner of his own doctrine, but to recognise that in the practice of homeopathy, as in that of every other art, it is often what is not advised which works.

We do not see in these casebooks what we might imagine to be the work of a 'Hahnemannian' prescriber. What we see, instead, is homeopathy in embryo, and we see its conceiver and deliverer in the process of learning how to be a homeopath. He was extremely experimental and unbound by his own dogma. Every time he made a prescription it was an adventure. He did not know what would happen and was often taken completely by surprise.

CASE ANALYSIS

It will be clear from the discussion so far that Hahnemann's methods of case analysis and remedy selection were quite different from those commonly employed today. In his day, concepts such as the 'constitution' or 'essence' of the patient were unknown. He was familiar with an early notion of constitution – that of diathesis[7] or predisposition to certain types of disease – and he occasionally used terms drawn from diathetic diagnosis, calling patients 'scrofulous' for instance, or 'lymphatic'. Claire Christallo, for example, was a three-year-old child 'disposed to scrofula'. At other times he referred to patients as being 'sanguine' or 'choleric', using the old humoral descriptions in which he had been schooled. Mme de la Nois was described as having a sanguine temperament, Eugène Perry as having a choleric character. M. le Comte de Quelin was also choleric.

However, Hahnemann does not appear to have used such diagnoses as an aid to prescribing. The concept of the 'constitutional remedy' incorporating healthy characteristics, which has played such an important part in the development of modern homeopathic prescribing, had not yet emerged, and he certainly did not normally take constitutional symptoms compatible with health into account when choosing his remedy. He prescribed largely on the basis of pathological symptoms, and the patient's physical pathology was taken fully into account and not regarded as subsidiary. In his own studies of the remedies he had, in fact, only just touched upon a notion which has since become the cornerstone of a certain school of homeopathic prescribing – the idea that people may fall into personality 'types' which conform to the 'picture' of a remedy.[8]

Nor was he a 'mentals' prescriber, at least not in the sense that we understand that expression today. There is no evidence in these casebooks that Hahnemann gave the enormously special weight to psychological symptoms that some modern prescribers do. Although in the *Organon* he wrote eloquently about the importance of such symptoms, he also stated clearly that this was because they tended to be more characteristic than others, not because they were psychological symptoms as such.[9] The prominent place given to these in modern homeopathy seems to have originated with Kent and his followers, half a century later, when they equated illness with sin, and disease with willingly turning away from God. Seeing all disease as being primarily an affection of the inner man, they necessarily saw inner, psychological symptoms as causative.[10]

In Hahnemann's time the vast potential of the remedies to deal with psychological states had not yet been fully realised. Though the provings of remedies had already elicited a good deal of psychological information, it seems that at this time, at any rate, this information exceeded what could be translated into terms applicable to the patient in front of the homeopath. In the early years of homeopathy, the years contemporary with and immediately after Hahnemann, the interpretation of materia medica tended to concentrate on physical pathology and clinical detail, exemplified in the works of Jahr, Boenninghausen,

Allen, Hering, Farrington and Boericke. It was only at a later date that a more constitutional or characterological perception of both patient and remedy action became common, exemplified in the works of Kent and Tyler, for instance. In more recent years, we have seen successive homeopaths tentatively building more psychological and characterological symptoms into the remedy pictures, learning how to use the more sophisticated awareness of the human mind and emotions which has been achieved over the last two hundred years. This is exemplified in the work of Vithoulkas, Catherine Coulter, Paschero, Candegabe and Sankaran.[11] However, even now, the use of psychological symptoms by homeopaths is still in a very undeveloped state.

If we are surprised at Hahnemann's relatively pathological approach, we need to realise that this is a function of time and period rather than of dogma. Although it was he who opened up the area of prescribing on psychological symptoms in the first place, he was, in this as in many of his observations, 'expert beyond experience'. At a time when the whole concept of psychosomatic illness was only just beginning to find expression, it is not surprising that Hahnemann and his contemporaries were slow to appreciate the depths of the implications of psychological proving symptoms. Hahnemann died thirteen years before Freud was born.

It would not be true to say that Hahnemann never prescribed on 'mental' symptoms. What it is important to realise is that he did so only when such symptoms were both pathological and highly characteristic of both patient and remedy. He prescribed Aurum to Mme Peigne, for instance, on the symptom of 'desire to commit suicide'. In Mme Peigne's case it was an active strong symptom and Hahnemann especially noted that it was the reason for the prescription of Aurum. In the case of Mme Durien, however, who had the same symptom, evoked by jealous suspicion of her husband, Hahnemann chose to prescribe a number of remedies, all apparently focussing on the sporadic physical symptom of a nervous tic. M. Laburthe, who had been well for nine months, was given Ignatia to inhale every other day when his old illness returned, quite clearly provoked by a 'vif chagrin'.

Although 'chagrin' or grief was frequently reported to Hahnemann as an important symptom, he did not invariably respond to it with, for instance, Ignatia rather than Sulphur, though he did so, of course, on some occasions. He prescribed Ignatia to Mme Delcambre, after the loss of her mother, and to Lady Drummond of Melford, who suffered from persistent grief after the loss of three children. He gave it to

Sheila Brugmann after she was reported to have been lamenting her unluckiness in love.

I have dwelt on this matter at some length because it seems to me to be important, in view of the tendency in some circles to see homeopathy as an absolute truth, rather than as a product of cultural accretions. Hahnemann was not an essence prescriber. He had not had the opportunity, which 150 years of collective clinical experience has now given to practitioners, to flesh out the pictures of remedies with psychological and characterological detail. He prescribed only on 'sick' symptoms, pathological symptoms, or symptoms which, while compatible with health, were not desirable, as in 'lachrymation while walking into the wind' or 'craving for the taste of charcoal'.

However, neither was he a specific or a symptomatic prescriber; he was not what we might derogatorily call a pathological prescriber. He prescribed on mental, physical, general or particular symptoms of a wide variety, but only when they were prominent. Symptoms such as desire to commit suicide, bloody stools, uterine haemorrhage and paralysis of single parts were all capable of being used as guiding indications to the remedies. What they had in common was that they were more or less characteristic of the patient, in that they were either a fundamental part of the patient's disease picture, or a peculiar and individualising aspect of the patient. And that they were also to some degree characteristic of a particular remedy.

Hahnemann was a gestalt prescriber, assuming that the foregrounded symptom implied the whole, that if he saw a trunk the animal was an elephant and not a tiger.

NOTES

1. See further Chapter 6.

2. Boenninghausen had produced several repertories including *Systematisch-alphabetisches Repertorium der homöopathischen Arzneien*, 2 editions, Münster 1832 and 1835.

3. Georg Jahr published first a *Handbuch der Hauptanzeigen für die richtige Wahl der homöopathischen Heilmittel*, Düsseldorf 1834 ('Der mittlere Jahr'), then two repertories incorporated into materia medica: *Ausführlicher Symptomen-Kodex der homöopathischen Arzneimittel-lehre*, Düsseldorf 1835, and a much expanded version of this with the same title published in Düsseldorf and Leipzig 1843–8 ('Der grosse Jahr'). This was translated into English by C. J. Hempel in 1848 and augmented by him in 1853 (see Bibliography). Later Jahr published *Klinische Anweisungen zu homöopathischer Behandlung der Krankheiten*, Leipzig 1849 ('Der kleine Jahr').

Jahr's *Nouveau Manuel* (the French version) was published as *Jahr's New Manual*, translated with extensive additions from various sources by C. J. Hempel, aided by James Quin, Vol. 1, New York 1848.

Hartlaub, Weber, Glazor, Peschier, Ruoff and Lafitte had all produced repertories of different kinds. For details see J. Kishore, 'The Repertories in General', *The Homoeopath*, Vol. 6 (3 and 4), London 1987. This article was originally published as the introduction to the second edition of the Kishore Cards.

Lafitte's seems to have been the earliest published French repertory: P. J. Lafitte, *Symptomatologie homoéopathique, ou tableau synoptique de toute la matière médicale pure.*Vol.1, Paris 1844.

4. Typical of the rubrics used are:

Mme Maurice:

Stecken im Brustbein: ang, arg, ars, aur, caust, chin, con, euph, mang, oleand, sab.

Brennen in der Brust: ars, kal, spong.

Gargouillement au creux de l'estomac: carb a, croc, laur, men, mos, thea, verb.

Apres le dîner chalcur: calc, + nit (nit ac), phos.

Muskelzucken: mag carb.

M. Lecointe:

Saurer Auswurf: Calc, mur, magn, ph, nat ph.

Mlle Brugmann:

Heftiges Schreien: bell, plat.

Lachen: hyos, crot, nux-m.

Mme Figuera:

Magenkrampf nach règles: kali-c.

Brûle et prurit aux parties gen: amb, am c, calc, carb v, kal, merc, zinc, acid nit, sulph, thuj.

5. He had already talked of this in *Organon*, 5th edn, paragraph 246 note 1, and there suggested the intercurrent use of Hepar Sulph. and Nux Vomica to respond to aggravations.

6. Hahnemann frequently notes the usefulness of alternation in acute disease and fevers in the course of his writings.

7. See Chapter 3, Note 13.

8. Hahnemann only twice made observations of this nature, in the commentary to the provings of Nux Vomica and Pulsatilla in *Materia Medica Pura*.

9. See *Organon*, 6th edn, paragraph 211, 'The psychic condition of the patient is often the decisive factor in choosing a homeopathic remedy, because it is a particularly characteristic symptom and one that can least of all remain hidden from the carefully observant physician.'

10. A brief study of the part played in the development of homeopathy by the religious beliefs of many of the early American homeopaths may be found in Francis Treuherz, 'The Origins of Kent's Homoeopathy', *Journal of the American Institute of Homeopathy*, Vol. 77, No. 4, December 1984, pp. 130–149. The article draws attention to the similarities between the ideas and philosophies of Emmanuel Swedenborg and the modifications introduced into the practice of homeopathy by influential Swedenborgian homeopaths in the late nineteenth century. The ideas and implications first presented in this article have been discussed further by A. Campbell, *The Two Faces of Homoeopathy*, London 1984 and P. Nicholls, *Homoeopathy and the Medical Profession*, London 1988.

11. See Bibliography for full details of works by these authors.

Chapter 5

Hahnemann's Materia Medica

What were the remedies which Hahnemann actually had at his disposal to aid him in his efforts to eliminate disease? How did he attempt to match the totality of symptoms after the action of Sulphur had been exhausted? What was his materia medica and how much information did he have about the remedies included in it?

We who have now nearly three thousand remedies, many with complex symptom pictures based on provings and expanded by a wealth of additional clinical information, can barely imagine Hahnemann's experience as he struggled to respond to a huge field of disease with, at first, a mere handful of remedies and far less information about their action than is available to us. We are accustomed to thinking of the materia medica as it is today, consisting of all the remedies and the vast accumulation of symptoms that we now know. To understand Hahnemann's task we have to go back in our imagination to the early days of homeopathy, when he and his fellow homeopaths had very few remedies, relatively poorly proved and augmented by very few clinical symptoms.

Even when he died, after nearly fifty years of developing homeopathy, Hahnemann was still working with fewer than two hundred remedies. Some of these he used extensively and some hardly at all, having reached different stages of development and understanding with each of them. He could only use his remedies to the extent that their symptomatology had become manifest; since this was a slow process of which he was the initiator, it seems obvious that Hahnemann must have used them in a much more restricted way than we do, or at least aspire to. We have seen some of the evidence of this limitation in the previous chapter.

He developed his materia medica in three ways, gaining information from provings, medical and chemical literature, and clinical experience. Initially he and his family, friends and colleagues proved a number of substances on themselves. Many of these substances were used in orthodox medicine and were probably selected because the experimenters already had some awareness of their symptomatology and therefore some perception of how useful they might be. Most of the remedies Hahnemann used in the early days of his practice, up to about 1828, fall into this category: they had been subject to provings conducted either by himself or by a colleague with Hahnemann's close participation. He therefore had an intimate knowledge of the action of these remedies. In the early days the remedies used were largely those which we now call acute or apsoric remedies.

Towards the end of this period he began to use remedies which he was later to describe as antipsoric – remedies capable of combatting the newly defined psoric miasm; after 1828, most of the remedies introduced into the materia medica were so described by him. Although some of the provings of these continued to be conducted by Hahnemann and his close colleagues, an increasing number of members of the homeopathic community became involved in the development of the materia medica and its amplification on the basis of clinical evidence. Throughout his practice, and naturally more so in the later years, he took advantage of other homeopaths' work and used remedies introduced by them. These remedies had sometimes been scrupulously proved, sometimes not. He occasionally even used remedies which appear to have been completely unproved.

EARLY PERIOD – TO 1828

The following are the remedies Hahnemann had developed during the first thirty years or so of his practice (the date given is the date when the remedy was first introduced into the materia medica):[1]

Aconitum (1805), Ambra Grisea (1827), Angustura Vera (1821), Argentum (1818), Argentum Nitricum (1818), Arnica (1805), Arsenicum Album (1816), Asarum Europaeum (1817), Auripigmentum (Orpiment) (1824), Aurum Foliatum (1818), Aurum Metallicum (1818), Belladonna (1805), Bismuthum Oxidum (1821), Bryonia Alba (1816), Calcarea Acetica (1819), Camphora (1805), Cannabis Sativa (1811), Cantharis (1805), Capsicum (1805), Carbo Animalis (1827), Carbo Vegetabilis (1827), Causticum (1805), Chamomilla (1805), Chelidonium (1818), China (1805), Cicuta Virosa (1821), Cina (1811), Cinnabaris (1811), Cocculus (1805), Colocynthis (1821), Conium (1818), Copaiva (1805), Cuprum Metallicum (1805), Cyclamen (1819), Digitalis (1805), Drosera

(1805), Dulcamara (1811), Euphrasia (1819), Ferrum Met. (1816), Guaiacum (1818), Helleborus (1805), Hepar Sulphuris Calcareum (1818), Hyoscyamus (1805), Ignatia (1805), Ipecacuanha (1805), Ledum (1805), Magnetis Arcticus (1816), Magnetis Australis (1816), Manganum (1821), Menyanthes (1819), Mercurius Aceticus (1811), Merc. Cor. (Merc. Subl.) (1811), Merc. Dulcis (1811), Merc. Praecipitatus Ruber (1811), Merc. Sol. (1811), Merc. Viv. (1811), Mezereum (1805), Moschus (1811), Mur. Ac. (1819), Nux Vom. (1805), Oleander (1817), Opium (1805), Phosphoric Acid (1819), Pulsatilla (1805), Rheum (1805), Rhus Tox. (1811), Ruta (1818), Sambucus (1819), Sarsaparilla (1818), Sepia (1817), Silica (1817), Spigelia (1819), Spongia (1821), Squilla (1817), Stannum (1821), Staphysagria (1819), Stramonium (1805), Sulphur (1818), Taraxacum (1819), Thuja (1819), Valerian (1805), Veratrum Album (1805), Verbascum (1821).

It is clear from this list that many of these early proven remedies have since become the core of the materia medica used by all homeopaths. Many of them were already used frequently by Hahnemann, as invaluable then as now. Remedies such as Aconite, Belladonna and Chamomilla were used in acute febrile conditions. Arnica was the injury remedy par excellence. Ignatia was widely used in response to grief and 'chagrin'. Valerian was invaluable as a general sedative. Arsenicum Album, Bryonia Alba, Causticum, Drosera and Ipecacuanha were often called upon in acute respiratory cases in the early days and were later supplemented in acutes by Dulcamara, Phosphorus and Spongia. Because respiratory problems were so rife and so difficult we often find Hahnemann using remedies experimentally in such cases. For instance, he used the poorly proved and even now little known Auripigmentum (or Orpiment) several times in serious cases.[2]

Arsenicum Album, Capsicum, Nux Vomica, Pulsatilla and Veratrum Album had long been used to respond to a multitude of mild digestive problems. As the years went by, Hahnemann added other acute 'digestive' remedies to his armamentorium and Carbo Animalis, Carbo Vegetabilis, Cina and Colocynthis became widely used on the basis of a number of digestive symptoms. Later Angustura Vera, Bismuthum Oxidum and Cicuta Virosa were drafted in experimentally, though used only occasionally and in very specific circumstances. Constipation was usually treated with either Nux Vomica or Opium, sometimes with Plumbum. His earliest proved remedy, China, was used extensively, especially in the field of general debility and women's ailments. Ferrum Metallicum also had an important application in these fields.

Bryonia, Causticum, Rhus Tox. and Ruta were commonly used in rheumatic conditions and we also find an extensive use of remedies such as Aurum and Guaiacum in patients afflicted by the gouty rheumatism characteristic of the age. Ledum, another remedy associated with gouty rheumatism, was, oddly enough, little used. Many of these early proved remedies reflect the paralytic and convulsive states commonly manifested in patients of the day: Camphora, Causticum, Cocculus, Cuprum Metallicum and later, Agaricus, Alumina, Ambra Grisea, Cicuta Virosa, Colocynthis, Conium, Oleander, Phosphoric Acid and Staphysagria. Here again, some remedies were introduced experimentally: Magnetis Polus Arcticus and Magnetis Polus Australis for instance. Hahnemann had experimented with the effects of passing the north and south poles of the magnet over the spine and observing the results. Despite taking the trouble to make this experiment and produce a remedy well-adapted to some of the neuralgic and paralytic symptoms frequently met with in his patients, he seems to have used these remedies only once, with Lord Elgin, who suffered from severe neuralgic pain.

Arsenicum Album, Cantharis and Copaiva were invaluable in the treatment of gonorrhoea and its sequelae. Later Cannabis Sativa, Petroselinum and, of course, Thuja expanded the range. Hyoscyamus, Stramonium and Veratrum Album were used on the rare occasions when Hahnemann was called upon to treat the mentally ill. They were also used in treating more prosaic complaints such as cramps and bowel disturbances.

Many remedies had not yet found their full range of expression. This was particularly true of remedies such as Pulsatilla and Sepia, whose great usefulness in the field of women's ailments had not yet been completely appreciated. In general, though the polychrests had been identified as such, much of their potential had yet to be realised and they were greatly underused. Silica, for instance, was for a long time seen largely as a remedy merely for suppuration and scrofulous conditions. Only in later years did it become used as a major antipsoric. Similarly, the extent of Arsenicum's usefulness had not been appreciated and its deployment was largely restricted to incidences of digestive upsets and burning pains. The use of Thuja was restricted almost entirely to cases of gonorrhoea and related urinary affections.

On the other hand, some remedies were a lot more commonly used

then than now. Cinnabar, Hepar Sulph. and the Mercuries were extensively prescribed in response to the predominance of syphilitic and
mercurial symptoms. Oleander is also frequently encountered. Not all
of the remedies he had actually proved were useful to Hahnemann
at this time. Several were never apparently called upon during the
Paris practice: Aurum Fol., Aurum Muriaticum, Calc. Acetica, Merc.
Aceticus, Merc. Dulcis, Merc. Praecipitatus Ruber, for instance. (Many
of these had received only a partial proving.) Others were used
infrequently: Angustura, Argentum, Argentum Nitricum, Asarum,
Bismuthum Oxidum, Chelidonium, Cyclamen, Digitalis, Euphrasia,
Helleborus, Hyoscyamus, Manganum, Menyanthes, Mezereum,
Muriatic Acid, Moschus, Rheum, Sambucus, Squilla, Taraxacum and
Verbascum, for instance.

Hahnemann was not alone in using these remedies very little. In a
contemporary materia medica his colleague Georg Jahr recorded their
generally restricted use, noting, for example, that Argentum had only
hitherto been used to counter angina caused by mercury poisoning;
that Chelidonium was little known despite being indicated in cases of
paralytic traction and paralysis in different parts of the body; that
Mezereum, though useful for the effects of mercury and bone pains
had not yet been used extensively; and that Stramonium was used
largely in convulsions, fits, spasmodic affections especially caused by
fright or respiration of the vapours of mercury.[3]

The awareness of the affinities of remedies to certain states and
diseases which Jahr shows in these comments may look like the
work of a pathological prescriber. However, it illustrates the normal
approach to materia medica which was widespread among early
homeopaths – the general disease state was used as a prescribing aid by
them as it was by Hahnemann, though, where possible, the specific
remedy was chosen on the basis of particularising symptoms.

In this early stage of the development of his materia medica,
Hahnemann also used remedies whose provings had been conducted
by others but in which he had taken part. As with the remedies whose
provings he had conducted himself, some quickly became favourites
while others were used only occasionally. Antimonium Tartaricum,
Asafoetida, Coffea, Colchicum, Sabadilla and Sabina, for instance,
soon became invaluable.

MIDDLE PERIOD – 1828 TO 1839

In later years, from 1828 almost until the end of his life, he began to produce descriptions of the remedies that he called antipsorics. He published pathogeneses of these in the various editions of *Chronic Diseases* between 1828 and 1839:[4]

Alumina (1835), Ammonium Carbonicum (1828), Anacardium (1835), Baryta Carbonica (1828), Borax (1835), Calcarea Acetica (1828), Calcarea Carbonica (1828), Clematis (1837), Graphites (1828), Iodum Purum (1828), Kali Carbonicum (1830), Lycopodium (1828), Magnesium Carbonicum (1828), Magnesium Muriaticum (1828), Natrum Carbonicum (1828), Natrum Muriaticum (1830), Nitric Acidum (1828), Nitrum (Kali Nitricum) (1838), Petroleum (1828), Petroselinum (1828), Phosphorus (1828), Sulphuric Acid (1839), Zincum (1828).

He also published in *Chronic Diseases* fuller descriptions of some remedies already proved, whether by him or others, reclassifying these as antipsorics and adding symptoms to their descriptions:

Agaricus (1835), Ammonium Muriaticum (1835), Antimonium Crudum (1835), Arsenicum Album (1816), Aurum (1818), Carbo Animalis (1827), Carbo Vegetabilis (1827), Causticum (1805), Colocynthis (1821), Conium (1818), Cuprum Metallicum (1805), Digitalis (1805), Dulcamara (1811), Guaiacum (1818), Hepar Sulphuris Calcareum (1818), Manganum (1821), Mezereum (1805), Muriaticum Acidum (1819), Phosphoric Acid (1819), Platina (1839), Sarsaparilla (1818), Sepia (1817), Silica (1817), Stannum (1821), Staphysagria (1819), Stramonium (1805), Sulphur (1818).

The origin of the pathogeneses of these remedies has long been a subject of dispute. It is far from clear that the descriptions are based on good provings and there is more than a strong suspicion that they are in fact largely based on clinical observations. Richard Hughes attempted to disentangle the various grades of symptoms in the descriptions of these remedies, separating proving symptoms from clinical symptoms, but his effort was doomed to failure.[5] In fact it is hardly possible to imagine that Hahnemann should not have augmented his remedy descriptions with evidence gained from clinical observation or 'cured symptoms'. In view of the fact that, by the time he wrote *Chronic Diseases*, he was conducting provings with potentised remedies, there was no reason why a 'cured symptom', achieved in a patient by means of a potentised remedy, should not be given equal weight with a proving symptom.

One of Hahnemann's most endearing characteristics is his habit of noting 'cured symptoms' in the margins of the casebooks, clearly quite delighted that his remedies worked in ways he had not anticipated from the provings. In Mme Maurice's case, he noted that Natrum Phosphoricum had got rid of the 'bitter taste in the mouth'. Ignatia, prescribed to Mme Bagdazar when she was unable to sleep because of 'serious thoughts', was noted as having cured her 'pains on movement'. Hahnemann wrote 'NB Guaj!' in the margin after Mr Lyster's lancinating pains in the heart and his gouty pains cleared up, only to be replaced by a sore throat. M. Leparcur was suffering badly from itching scabs on the legs. His digestion was bad and he was finding it difficult to sleep. He was generally much better from Euphorbium and Hahnemann wrote '!!' in the margin. M. Lecointe's diarrhoea was better for Phosphorus and his eye for Isopath. Manganum alleviated Mme de Comogne's pains in the stomach, according to a note, and Hahnemann wrote a triumphant 'Borax!!' when Mme le Varcy improved on it. She had had great pain in her tongue as well as aphthae which prevented her from speaking.

As was the case with the earlier remedies, some of these more recently proved antipsorics came into immediate frequent use and can be seen everywhere in Hahnemann's casebooks, whereas others took time to make their presence felt and perhaps never achieved more than a local use. Alumina, Ammonium Muriaticum and Carbonicum, Calcarea Carbonica, Graphites, Kali Carbonicum, Lycopodium, Magnesium Carbonicum and Muriaticum, Natrum Muriaticum, Nitricum Acidum, Phosphorus, Platina and Zinc, for instance, appear regularly and, as the years go by, find their position as important remedies, being used in an increasingly wider context. Ammonium Muriaticum and Carbonicum enjoyed a vogue which has since declined. It is worth noting that the smelling-salt *sal volatile* was an Ammonium and was frequently used during this period. One wonders how much this contributed to the widespread appearanccof the remedy picture. The extensive use of the homeopathic Magnesiums was also presumably related to the widespread use of their allopathic counterparts to counter digestive disturbances among the population.

Platina began to be used frequently in the course of time but had yet to find its full range, and it was largely prescribed by Hahnemann on general physical symptoms. This is true of most of these remedies which now form such an important part of the homeopathic corpus. Calcarea Carbonica, Graphites, Kali Carbonicum and Natrum Muriaticum were largely used in digestive conditions, Lycopodium and Phosphorus in respiratory conditions, for example. Alumina and Zincum were most commonly used in response to paralytic conditions.

Other recently developed remedies, such as Agaricus, Anacardium, Antimonium Crudum, Baryta Carbonica, Borax, Clematis, Euphorbium, Iodum, Natrum Carbonicum, Nitrum, Petroleum and Sulphuricum Acidum were used in a more restricted way – indeed, some have still not achieved a wide understanding. Agaricus was used largely in cases of epilepsy. Anacardium was surprisingly little used when one considers that its main general features correspond so well to some of the common states reported in the casebooks. Though Boenninghausen later commented that it was almost exclusively adapted to ill-natured persons, and Jahr noted its 'alienation of mind and insanity',[6] Hahnemann normally prescribed it on more physical indications. Borax was, as it still is, largely restricted to use in digestive problems, as was Antimonium Crudum. Similarly, Natrum Carbonicum was only used in digestive cases despite the wider symptom picture already known. Clematis was only used once, in a case of suppressed gonorrhoea, despite its theoretically wider application. Nitrum (Kali Nitricum) had an occasional application in severe respiratory cases. Sulphuricum Acidum was used only twice. Petroleum scarcely appears at all.

It is clear that Hahnemann's focus when prescribing differed from ours. With so few remedies, the main aim of his work, and of those following him closely, was to expand the capacity of the materia medica. It was for later homeopaths to explore ways of expanding its understanding. In these casebooks we see evidence of willingness to experiment in the interest of increasing the number of remedies in the materia medica. Although he followed his own advice and used symptoms based on his own provings where he could, Hahnemann was a notable experimentalist and would try anything once. We can see several examples of this, when he prescribes a remedy with only a limited proving, or one proved by someone other than him – even occasionally not proved or written about at all, just intelligently studied. He did this increasingly in the latest period of his practice, an even more empirical phase than previously, one in which he was willing to take on trust the provings or clinical experience of others.

LATE PERIOD – AFTER 1839

Most of the people responsible for introducing these new remedies into the materia medica had been close colleagues of his and he presumably felt he could trust them. Drs Stapf, Hartlaub, Trinks, Noack and Hering all made substantial contributions to the development of the materia medica, organising the publication of new remedy pictures drawn from provings and poisoning symptoms gathered by many practitioners all over the world. In Stapf's *Archives* and, later, his *Materia Medica*, Hahnemann would have found descriptions of remedies such as Agnus Castus, Colchicum, Crocus Sativa, Senega, Teucrium Marum and Zingiber, which he eagerly took up. In Hartlaub and Trinks' *Materia Medica*, published at more or less the same time, he would have found Aethusa, Antimonium Crudum, Asafoetida, Borax, Bovista, Coffea, Gratiola, Indigo, Jalapa, Laurocerasus, Natrum Sulphuricum, Paris Quadrifolia, Phellandrium, Plumbum, Ratanhia, Sabadilla, Sabina, Secale Cornutum, Strontium Carbonicum, Tabacum and Zincum.[7] He also used remedies introduced by that energetic prover Constantine Hering in South America: Crotalus Horridus, Lachesis, Mercurius Vivus, Psoricum (the early name for Psorinum), Sanguinaria, Selenium and Theridion.[8]

Remedies developed by a variety of other homeopaths included Berberis, Croton Tiglium, Kreosotum, Nux Moschata, Ranunculus Bulbosus, Ranunculus Sceleratus, Rhododendron and Viola Tricolor. Other remedies used by Hahnemann, despite the fact that a formal proving had not yet appeared, included Diadem, Dictamnus Albus, Jaborandi, Melilotus, Murex Purpurea, Hippozaeninum, Saponinum and Nitri Spiritus Dulcis. Though none of these was officially proved until some time after his death, it is possible that he had had access to some early unpublished experiments.[9]

The motive behind the adoption of such new remedies was always, of course, to cure. Hahnemann would choose a relatively unknown remedy and use it on a patient whose progress under better-known remedies had halted. Some such remedies subsequently gained a wide application, others remained obscure. Lachesis soon became widely used, though not, at first, in the treatment of women's ailments where it has proved so valuable in recent times. Crocus Sativa was used selectively but intensively in certain 'women's' complaints. Murex Purpurea and Secale Cornutum, with their haemorrhagic tendencies, also found an application in this field, as did Crotalus Horridus, Kreosotum and Melilotus.

Gratiola, Jaborandi, Jalapa and Plumbum were all used mainly for problems with digestion and stool, all proving indispensable in indicated cases. Hahnemann also swiftly took up the use of new remedies affecting the nervous system: Aethusa and Laurocerasus appear with some regularity. Jahr recorded that Laurocerasus was used only against cyanosis, phthisis florescens and cholera.[10] However, Hahnemann's use of it reflected a wider understanding of the remedy, and he seems to have prescribed it on some of its more characteristic symptoms: 'Great anxiety, apprehension and agitation which do not allow a moment's rest . . . froth at the mouth. Deglutition is hindered or obstructed.'[11] The little-known Indigo with its marked action on the nervous system was also introduced into his practice at this time.

Other newly-introduced remedies were Agnus Castus, which rapidly became an invaluable gonorrhoea remedy; Bovista, whose chief symptoms were eczematous eruptions on the skin; Colchicum and Rhododendron, augmenting the already large store of often-needed rheumatic remedies; Saponinum supplemented these on the one occasion when it exactly fitted the symptoms.[12] Natrum Sulphuricum, which had acquired an early reputation only for 'intermittent fever' joined the armamentorium. Nux Moschata came into occasional use with its marked tendency to fainting fits and heart failure along with irresistible drowsiness. Later it was joined by Nitri Spiritus Dulcis, an even more somnolent remedy.

Many of these remedies only made a token appearance in the casebooks, being brought in occasionally for very specific use: Phellandrium, which became known as a good remedy for the offensive expectoration and cough in phthisis, bronchitis and emphysema appears once, as does Diadem Aranea. Ratanhia was introduced to help a patient with rectal problems and Croton Tiglium was used with the same patient. Ranunculus Bulbosus appears occasionally, more often than its cousin Ranunculus Sceleratus. Selenium became an effective toothache remedy, while Senega had an application in diseases of the mucous membranes. Strontium Carbonicum was only used for digestive problems though it had rheumatic pains, threatened apoplexy and violent involuntary starts in its picture. Tabacum was given on the symptom of 'body feels bruised'. Teucrium Marum had an occasional application in catarrhal conditions and polyps. Dictamnus Albus seems to have been generally unknown, and Jahr wrote that it was only found in the nomenclature of our materia medica because Hahnemann had mentioned it in the *Organon* in connection with leucorrhoea with slimy mucus.[13] This, indeed, was the single symptom on which Hahnemann prescribed it (once) in the casebooks.

Hahnemann was also willing *in extremis* to use remedies which were unproved. Auto was a remedy prepared, as needed, from the patient's own sputum. He used it only in stubborn cases of phthisis or other advanced affections of the respiratory system, where it usually brought about a temporary amelioration. He gave it, for example, to the tubercular patients Mme Morrisse and Mme Lebauche in a series of different potencies. He also gave it to the 4-year-old Marie Legouvé when she was slow to recover after having scarlet fever. And to Mrs Boddington.

He used Isopath, another remedy prepared from the patient's own disease product, in similar circumstances, giving it to M. Lecointe when no other remedies were able to ameliorate his condition. He also used Antepilept, presumably a nosode, when faced with severe epilepsy in the case of Mlle Langston. His rare use of the nosode Psoricum was reserved for similar, often terminal cases. It gave M. Lascour an extra lease of life when prescribed for him.

Oxymuriatic Acid (Chlorine) was used mainly in stubborn respiratory affections. It was not proved at the time and seems to have appeared in no materia medica until Boericke noted its marked effect on the respiratory organs, producing spasms of the glottis and constriction with suffocation. He called it Chlorum.[14] This remedy was developed by Hahnemann from a contemporary product and was usable without a proving, presumably because its symptoms were so well known. The consumptive M. Lecointe was given it after Phosphorus had ceased to improve his inflamed eye. The Oxymuriatic Acid in fact aggravated the eye even more. Mme Videl and M. Lelaisse were both prescribed it.

Nitri Spiritus Dulcis (alcoholised nitric ether) was another remedy based on a common contemporary product. This ether was not quite the same as the ether whose anaesthetic qualities were just beginning to be recognised, but it had much the same symptom picture. Hahnemann had recommended it for use in the hospital typhus epidemic of 1813.[15] In the casebooks he used it only once, desperately seeking to help Miss Stirling, whose condition had not been ameliorated by a whole host of soporific remedies including Moschus and Nux Moschata.

Ozaena, which likewise appears only once, must be the remedy Hippozaeninum, first written about by Dr Peschier in 1834[16] but not apparently fully proved until much later.[17] Hahnemann gave it to a M. Chauchot, who had had a 'spasmodic affection' for seven years. He now had a chest problem and had been spitting blood for five months. He had polyps in his nose and his body was covered with itching liver spots. Hahnemann gave him Sulphur and other remedies without improvement and then hazarded Ozaena, which improved things considerably. Later he told his patient to apply Ozaena to the skin.

What we see here is Hahnemann slowly expanding his materia medica. It seems that in the early years of provings, he experimented with remedies which were commonly used in allopathic medicine and discovered their homeopathic potential. As the years went by he seems to have chosen to experiment with substances which might be expected to yield symptoms corresponding to some of the symptoms most commonly met with in his practice, and so the remedies he proved later on tended to become very reliable members of his armamentorium. This did not happen immediately and the remedies proved later, or by others, were used very variably. Jahr's *New Manual*, first published in 1840, contains several small remedies which Hahnemann never prescribed.

He prescribed all these remedies in very much the same way as he always had: on the basis of characteristic symptoms when he could find them, or on less important but persistent symptoms where he could not. The only difference that the adoption of the initial prescription of Sulphur seems to have made was that it delayed the process of prescribing according to individual symptoms for a while, and that Sulphur was often reverted to as a base-line remedy. However, we can also begin to discern a rather hazy difference in his attitude to the two grades of remedy he had created: apsoric and antipsoric. The apsoric remedies do on the whole seem to be restricted to minor and acute illnesses, such as fever, coryza or injury, whereas the antipsoric ones were increasingly used in response to recurring or latent chronic symptoms on the whole, and were used for longer periods and in a sequence of potencies.

It is clear that Hahnemann was at this point in his career only using the smallest fraction of the capacity of some of his remedies, basing his prescriptions on marked or characteristic physical symptoms in a quite narrow range. This may seem odd to us, for the greatest advances in the study of materia medica in recent times have taken place in the development of the application of remedies according to their psychological symptoms. The approach to materia medica has changed radically since Hahnemann's day as a result of successive attempts to expand and deepen our understanding of these remedies. In his time they appeared merely as sets of symptoms. Despite his adjuration to perceive the totality of the symptoms, he was in reality restricted to trying simply to cover as many important symptoms as possible. It has been the work of later homeopaths which has led us to the point where now we talk of the character and psychological types of remedies.

From Boenninghausen's initial expansion of understanding by means of the Doctrine of Analogy and the introduction of the use of concomitant symptoms, through Hering's *Guiding Symptoms* and Guernsey's *Keynotes* we have come to Kent's remedy pictures, Tyler's *Drug Pictures* and the modern approaches of Vithoulkas, Coulter and Sankaran. All these writers seek in their various ways to reach into the heart of the remedy, to discover its essence – its true keynotes – and even to extrapolate from this the 'normal' or sub-clinical characteristics of the patient needing the remedy.

The comparison between Hahnemann's methods and some modern methods is revealing. The shock that some of us may feel, at what often looks like pathological prescribing on Hahnemann's part, draws attention to the extent to which many prescribers now occupy a quite opposite position to this: prescribing so much on 'mentals' as almost to ignore the physical pathology in making a prescription. Nowadays emphasis on the 'mentals' can often seem interpretative rather than imaginative, and an over-ingenious psychologising may sometimes lead us away from the fundamental truth that the body and mind are one. If the nineteenth century stressed the physical over the psychological and spiritual aspects of the human being, the twentieth century is now in danger of swinging to the opposite pole. For many modern homeopaths the physical body appears to have come to be seen almost as a projection of the mind, despite the increasingly exciting research work demonstrating a far more subtle mind-body relationship.

NOTES

1. Most of the provings of these remedies first appeared in *Materia Medica Pura*. For further details and for this chronology see the article by J. Schmidt, 'Die Materia Medica Samuel Hahnemanns', in *Jahrbuch des Instituts für Geschichte der Medizin der Robert Bosch Stiftung*, Vol. 6,pp. 111–27, Stuttgart 1987. Although the article is not completely accurate, it is a useful approach to the study of Hahnemann's materia medica.

See also T. F. Allen, *Encyclopedia of Pure Materia Medica*, Philadelphia 1874–79 and Constantine Hering, *The Guiding Symptoms of our Materia Medica*, Philadelphia 1879, for an extensive collation of provings and sources of symptoms.

The following is a list of the remedies Hahnemann had proved or written about, arranged in chronological sequence of his first written notice of them (the dates are based on Schmidt's article):

1805: Aconite, Arnica, Belladonna, Camphor, Cantharis, Capsicum, Causticum, Chamomilla, China, Cocculus, Copaiva, Cuprum, Digitalis, Drosera, Helleborus, Hyoscyamus, Ignatia, Ipecacuanha, Ledum, Mezereum, Nux Vomica, Opium, Pulsatilla, Rheum, Stramonium, Valerian, Veratrum Album.

1811: Cannabis Sativa, Cina, Cinnabar, Dulcamara, Merc. Sol., Merc. Ac., Merc. C., Merc. D., Merc. P.-R., Mosch.

1816: Arsenicum Album, Bryonia, Ferrum Met., Magnet. Arct., Magnet. Aust., Rhus Tox.

1817: Asarum, Oleander, Sepia, Silica, Squilla.

1818: Arg., Arg. Nit., Aurum, Aurum-f, Aurum-m, Chelidonium, Conium, Guaj., Hepar Sulph., Ruta, Sarsaparilla, Sulphur.

1819: Calc. Ac., Cyclamen, Euphrasia, Menyanthes, Mur. Ac., Phos. Ac., Samb., Spigelia, Staphysagria, Tarax, Thuja.

1821: Angustura, Bismuth, Cicuta Virosa, Colocynthis, Manganum, Spongia, Stannum, Verbascum.

1824: Auript.

1827: Ambra Grisea, Carbo An., Carbo Veg.

1828: Amm. Carb., Bar. Ac., Bar. Carb., Calc. Carb., Graph., Iodum, Lycopodium, Mag. Carb., Mag. Mur., Nat. Carb., Nitric Acid, Petrol, Petroselinum, Phosphorus, Zincum.

1830: Kali Carb, Nat. Mur.

1835: Agaricus, Alumina, Amm. Mur., Anacardium, Ant. Crud., Borax.

1837: Clematis, Euphorbium.

1838: Kali Nit.

1839: Platina, Sul. Ac.

2. Hahnemann's short proving of Auripigmentum (sometimes written Orpiment in the casebooks) in *Materia Medica Pura* notes:

While walking in the open air a severe giddiness in the whole head as from intoxication. Stupefaction of the whole head. Too many irrelevant things occurred to him.

Throbbing stitches on the right side of the forehead. Needle pricks externally on the right side of the forehead.

Eye gum in the canthi of the eyes.

89

On chewing the food the teeth were painful as if they were loose.
At noon after eating violent nausea.
In the morning on waking violent cutting in the abdomen as from a chill.
Needle pricks from within outwards in the right side of the chest.
In the evening on going to sleep a fright as if he fell out of bed.

Hahnemann prescribed it to Ferdinand de Vere after the latter had had an epileptic attack with convulsions and drowsiness lasting about five minutes. Mlle St. Ouen had developed a great sensitivity in her chest after being given Stannum and so was given Auripigmentum 30c, followed by Auripigmentum 24c and the sensitivity decreased. Hahnemann also prescribed Auripigmentum to Mme Ferino when she had uterine problems and burning pains in the urethra on urination. Mme Delcambre's asthmatic condition had improved a little on Arsenicum but became much better after Auripigmentum.

3. See G. H. G. Jahr, *Nouveau manuel de médecine homoéopathique*, Paris 1840–41, translated by J. Laurie as *Manual of Homoeopathic Medicine*, London 1841.

4. S. C. F. Hahnemann, *Die chronischen Krankheiten*, Dresden 1828 and 1830, Leipzig 1835–9.

5. Richard Hughes, *passim* but especially his annotated version of *Hahnemann's Chronic Diseases*. See Bibliography.

6. Jahr *op. cit.*

7. Hartlaub and Trinks, *Reine Arzneimittellehre*, 3 vols, Leipzig 1828–31.

8. Constantine Hering, *The Guiding Symptoms of our Materia Medica*, Philadelphia 1879.

9. Details of the earliest attempts at provings or notices of these remedies are recorded in the *Materia Medica* of Constantine Hering and Timothy Allen. (See Bibliography).

10. Jahr, *op. cit.*

11. *ibid.*

12. Saponinum was given to Jules Daille after Manganum had elicited the following symptoms: 'His left knee was a little swollen, the other was alright. Redness on edge of eyelids, whites of eyes red, stiffness of arms and wrists.' After taking Saponinum the patient got a lot better and continued to take it for a while after.

13. Laurie, *op. cit.*, There is also a small entry in the 1848 Hempel translation of Jahr's *New Manual* which gives a few symptoms (it is not clear to what extent this description represents a proving): 'Aggravation of the epileptic fit (disappearing afterwards, curative effect). Profuse sweat. Frequent emission of large volumes of foetid flatulence. Increased stool. Costiveness. Increased secretion of urine. Profuse metrorrhagia for nine days (returning after ten days under continued use of the drug and lasting a few days with some debility). Itching of the anus and discharge of tenacious mucus from the uterus, at first brown and then white, lastly streaked with blood. Increased leucorrhoea with frequent discharge of urine, troublesome tenesmus and painful erosion of the pudendum (disappearing afterwards, curative effect).'

Mme Sanson was given Dictamnus Albus on the symptom of leucorrhoea.

14. Chlorine was known by the name of oxymuriatic acid from the time of its discovery in 1796. It acquired the name chlorine in 1810 but Hahnemann may well have continued to use the old chemical name. The fact that it seems to have been used mainly in stubborn respiratory affections supports this identification. I am grateful to Mr Robert Nichols for pointing out the probable equivalence of these two remedies to me.

15. Jahr describes it in his *New Manual*. In the 1848 edition of Jahr's *New Manual* Hempel quotes from Noack and Trinks' *Manual*: 'During the hospital typhus of 1813 Hahnemann recommended this agent for the following symptoms: indolence of the internal sensus communis, a sort of semi-paralysis of the mind; the patient lies quiet without sleeping or talking; he scarcely answers any questions even when urged, he appears to hear without understanding, the few words he utters are uttered with a low tone of voice and are *rational*. He cured the following symptoms resulting from the abuse of common table salt: Pale face and sunken eyes, langour, emaciation, extreme ill-humour; discouragement, disposition to quarrel and to be vehement, want of disposition to talk or work; heat in the mouth, contractive sensation in the throat and as if a plug were in the throat. Sour and slimy vomiting generally two hours after eating, followed by headache; repletion and pressure in the stomach after eating, with contractive sensation; chilliness over the whole body, after vomiting; a good deal of chilliness in the back. Tearing in the back from above downwards. Aggravation in the afternoon, irregular and scanty menses, hands covered with warts.' Miss

Stirling appears to have been the only patient who was prescribed this remedy, just as she was the only person to have Moschus and one of the few to have Nux Moschata.

16. Jahr does not mention this remedy in his writings but Dr Peschier wrote of Hippozaeninum in an article published in *Bibliothèque homoéopathique de Genève*, Vol. 3, 1834, p. 366. I am grateful to Dr Baur for drawing this to my attention.

17. In his *Materia Medica*, Clarke writes of Hippozaeninum only that 'The nosode has been used by homeopaths, at the suggestion of Garth Wilkinson, on the phenomena of the disease as guides (a horse disease, glanders) and in a large number of cases involving low forms of suppuration and catarrh, malignant ulcerations and swellings, abscesses and enlarged glands; and also in conditions similar in kind but less in severity. I have used it with excellent effect in cases of inveterate nasal catarrh and of glandular enlargement. The nasal affection may go onto ozaena, ulceration of nasal cartilages and bones.'

Chapter 6

The Venereal Miasms

We have now seen the full range of remedies to which Hahnemann had access to combat the disease symptoms remaining after he had 'cleared' the psoric miasm with Sulphur. What emerged after the administration of Sulphur was frequently a layer of venereal disease. As has already been remarked, Hahnemann himself wrote very little about the venereal miasms syphilis and sycosis, though he had been one of the first to identify them as sources of chronic disease.[1] It remained for later homeopaths to flesh out his theory with respect to the influence of these two great chronic diseases, which appear to have been almost as out of control in mid-nineteenth century Paris as is Aids in the late twentieth century.

In the 1840s Georg Jahr wrote of his surprise that his teacher had not completely developed his theories with regard to the chronic effect of venereal diseases, and conjectured that this was because he had not seen the widespread devastation they wrought in a large city.[2] This was indeed probably true until Hahnemann went to Paris, but through his casebooks we can see for ourselves how much he was confronted there with the misery these diseases brought to patients. Despite his not having developed the theory completely, much of Hahnemann's practical work in Paris was devoted to freeing his patients from the symptoms of venereal disease, which often overlay or exacerbated the simpler symptoms of psora.

Countless patients appear suffering either from what is now identified as gonorrhoea, with its well-known burning urine and gleety discharge, or from the chancres and ulcerations of syphilis, or from the far more subtle effects of latent syphilis related to the chancre which they confessed to having once had. In fact, the two diseases were not adequately differentiated at this time and tend to merge into one in patients' descriptions.

GONORRHOEA

Gonorrhoea had been epidemic since the recent Napoleonic wars. It was characterised by the appearance of 'fig-shaped' ('sycotic') condylomata around the genitals and a thick pussy discharge (though some forms did not have this). The common contemporary treatment was local applications of sabina powder, alum or tannin. The excrescences would not disappear as a result of these but only by being cauterised, either with fire or chemicals (commonly chromic or mercuric acid). Hahnemann, in common with other contemporary doctors, maintained that their suppression was usually followed by their return, either locally or at a distance.

SYPHILIS

Many patients reported having had a chancre at some stage in their life and so can be assumed to have had latent syphilis. The effects of syphilis were various and widespread. At first nothing might be noticed other than the tell-tale chancre at the site of infection. This soon disappeared, and if the patient were lucky he might experience little more than some kind of malaise and mild fever a few weeks later. It was even possible that there would be no more symptoms. However, it was beginning to be recognised in orthodox medicine that syphilis was a disease which first went underground and then returned in a far more terrible form, bringing with it various destructive effects on the nervous system (leading to headaches, nervous exhaustion, lightning pains, impotence, various forms of paralysis and incontinence), on the blood vessels (leading to heart conditions, early stroke), or on the brain (leading to epilepsy, general paralysis of the insane (GPI) and possibly mania). Many of Hahnemann's patients show the affections of blood vessels and nervous system which we now recognise to be the expression of tertiary syphilis. There are frequent reports of various paralyses, adult onset epilepsy, neurasthenic states, and some examples of the mania characteristic of the stage in the disease at which syphilis may attack the brain. Mercury, and later potassium iodide, was the only effective orthodox treatment for the disease.

SYPHILIS AND SYCOSIS

We can already discern the active presence of syphilitic and sycotic miasms from the frequency with which remedies associated with these conditions were prescribed, even in the absence of a fully developed theory with respect to these two miasms. Once Hahnemann had cleared the psoric miasm with Sulphur, he often found waiting there a ready-made syphilitic layer, a layer of venereal disease, or a layer of the mercurial treatment for it. (It is frequently hard to distinguish between disease and treatment.) In nearly every case he was obliged to use one of the major antimercurial or syphilitic remedies. The remedies he used most frequently therefore were not the polychrests we know so well today, but remedies like Alumina, Asafoetida, Aurum, Cinnabar, Clematis, Hepar Sulph., Mercurius Solubilis, Nitric Acid, Platina, Staphysagria – remedies given in response to ulceration, caries, necrosis of the bone, paralysis and suicidal despair. Next came Agnus Castus, Cannabis, Cantharis, Copaiva, Petroselinum, Senega, Selenium and Thuja, remedies to combat the endemic gonorrhoea and the endless genito-urinary disturbances which were its heirs. These are the remedies with which Hahnemann treated many of his cases.

The frequent use of Hepar Sulph., Mercurius Solubilis and Cinnabar is particularly marked. Hepar Sulphuris Calcareum was in some respects a remedy which bridged the psoric and syphilitic states. Nowadays the remedy seems to be thought of as predominantly psoric, containing, as it does, elements of the two great antipsorics Sulphur and Calcarea Carbonica. However, in this early period of homeopathy it was clearly perceived as a major remedy for the syphilitic/mercurial miasm. Inflammation, swelling, suppuration, buboes, ulceration, drawing pains and bleeding are prominent in its contemporary symptom picture, and it was known as being useful for 'evil consequences from the abuse of mercury'.[3] It was a remedy with which Hahnemann might sometimes open a case in preference to Sulphur.

Dr Quin, for instance, who had already taken a lot of remedies for his arthritis and asthma by the time he consulted Hahnemann, was given first Hepar Sulph., then Sulphur, then Cinnabar. Mr William Leaf had, amongst other remedies, Hepar Sulph., which considerably ameliorated his skin eruption. Dr Des Guidi had Hepar Sulph. followed by Mercurius Solubilis, for his digestive problems accompanied by copious diarrhoea.

The suppurative qualities of Hepar Sulph. were well appreciated. It was repeatedly prescribed to Mme Deville, who was suffering from a chronically swollen and painful arm caused by the application of leeches. It was also a remedy frequently indicated for the suppurative stage of phthisical complaints. M. Lascour had been coughing and spitting for a long time when he first visited the Hahnemanns. When he developed pain and inflammation in all the joints, suffocating feelings on walking and ascending, along with difficult respiration, Hahnemann prescribed Hepar Sulph. M. Lecointe, another young man suffering from phthisis, was given a lot of Hepar Sulph., with some success, as the disease entered its suppurative stage. The remedy was also used in less serious cases: when Mlle Saussarde came with swollen and suppurating sub-maxillary glands and painful glands in the breast, Hahnemann began prescribing with Hepar Sulph. and continued with this, despite the patient's feeling no better. Eighteen days later there was a slight improvement and after five weeks the glands had improved and remained better. Mme Aubertin was told to alternate the remedy with Nux Vomica when she had a catarrhal fever.[4]

Mercurius Solubilis was also commonly used, and given what we have seen about the extent of syphilis and mercury poisoning in Hahnemann's day, it is clear why it should have been needed frequently. Hahnemann had, in fact, noted the similarity of its symptoms to those of syphilis a year before he made the same connection between the symptoms of malaria and china. Its symptom picture is one that was commonly seen among his patients: general restlessness, nightly tearing pains, debility and weakness, ulceration and inflammation generally, inflammation and induration of glands, copious saliva, sweating and discharges, painful bones. He often prescribed it when a lot of allopathic mercury had been used in a case, or when the patient admitted to having had, and suppressed, a syphilitic chancre. Hahnemann seemed to have preferred, however, to wait until such a suppressed chancre reappeared in the course of treatment, rather than to prescribe for it automatically as he did with Sulphur. It was also used in response to transient and acute symptoms from its picture: Mme Grisenoi, for instance, was given Mercurius Solubilis when she had a fever with a little frisson every other night without thirst or sweat but with heat.

Very occasionally other mercurial remedies were used. Mercurius Corrosivus (called Mercurius Sublimatus by Hahnemann) was preferred in the case of Mme Leloir, who suffered from sporadic paralysis of larynx, throat and eyelids and the fingers of the right hand. Mme Leloir was given Mercurius Sublimatus when a stubborn sore throat, itching in the ears and swollen tonsils developed. This condition persisted and eventually over a long period the symptoms of paralysis appeared; Mercurius Sublimatus was prescribed quite frequently, intercalated among other remedies having symptoms of paralysis. From Boenninghausen's contemporary *Materia Medica* it is clear that the paralytic symptoms of Mercurius Corrosivus were much more appreciated at the time than those of Mercurius Solubilis. Mercurius Vivus was used very occasionally and was given, for example, to Marion Russell, deliberately substituted for Merc. Sublimatus.

Cinnabar was frequently used although it was not a well-known remedy at this time. Boenninghausen does not include it in his *Materia Medica*, and Jahr reports that it had only been employed against 'sycotic excrescences'. Hahnemann however had proved it, and his use of it anticipates Clarke's later comment that it 'corresponds to sycosis as well as to syphilis'.[5] Prominent symptoms are ulceration, bleeding warts and chancres, severe shooting pains, especially around the eye, and redness of the whole eye.

Hahnemann prescribed the remedy for Dr Quin, on the basis of the specific Cinnabar symptom of 'rheumatic pain in right knee joint, worse when walking, better at rest',[6] despite having repertorised four other symptoms which did not produce a single mention of this remedy. Here he was presumably also responding to Quin's history of venereal disease. When Hahnemann prescribed Cinnabar to Mr Campbell, the 'venereal' pustules on his face began to clear. Mme Leloir was given Cinnabar on the basis of the repertorised symptom of leucorrhoea (*fleurs blanches*). However, by the time it was prescribed for her she was suffering from intermittent semi-paralysis of various parts, including the eyelids, and her gums had begun to bleed. The Cinnabar improved the paralysis a little (though it did not affect the leucorrhoea), and the remedy was continued for a while. Some time later Hahnemann again began to prescribe it in a sequence with Mercurius Solubilis and Phosphoric Acid when the paralysis had become the dominant symptom in her condition.

Mr. Lyster was prescribed Cinnabar extensively in a number of different potencies. The initial prescription was made on the basis of lancinating pains in the heart, although he also suffered greatly from some of the effects of venereal disease – gouty arthritis and amaurosis; the remedy helped. M. Musard was prescribed it at one point and temporarily, at least, the pain in his liver went away 'because of the Cinnabar', as Hahnemann noted with pleasure in the casebook (page 187). Mme Deville was given Cinnabar for quite some time, probably on account of the lancinating pain associated with the nodes in her swollen arm. Mme Durien had suffered from *tic douleureux* for a long time and finally improved on the remedy. The casebook notes say that 'she is less well on the days when she does not take the Cinnabar'.

Many of the other remedies which Hahnemann used frequently in these casebooks also have a symptom picture which strongly reflects the effects of syphilis or mercury poisoning: remedies with affinities to the nervous system were probably far more commonly used then than now. Frequently encountered are: Agaricus, Alumina, Ambra Grisea, Arnica, Camphor, Causticum, Cocculus Indicus, Conium, Cuprum Metallicum, Guaiacum, Laurocerasus, Oleander, Platina, and Zincum Metallicum.

Because 'nervous' conditions were so common, Hahnemann had often to call on unusual, rare or new remedies to deal with intractable conditions, so we also find the following remedies occasionally used in this context: Aethusa, Argentum, Chelidonium, Colchicum, Colocynthis, Indigo, Magnetis Polus Arcticus, Magnetis Polus Australis, Manganum, Menyanthes, Mezereum, Spigelia and Valerian.

Lord Elgin (of Marbles fame) had been one of Hahnemann's earliest patients, and he remained so until he died in 1841. He suffered from serious damage to his nervous system as the result of mercury treatment. He was given a great number of remedies over the years, including Ambra Grisea, Asafoetida, Camphor, Causticum, Conium, Nux Vomica, Oleander, Opium, Platina, Ruta, Stannum, Staphysagria and Zincum, as well as the newer remedies: Aethusa, Indigo and both poles of the magnet.

Lord Elgin seems to have been one of the few patients to whom Hahnemann prescribed Indigo in the casebooks. He also resorted to the use of magnets with this patient alone. In desperation over his neuralgic pain, Lord Elgin was instructed to apply the magnet in the region of the fourth to sixth dorsal vertebrae at a distance of four or five finger breadths from the body, touching the painful place with one of the poles for as long as was necessary. He had an unhelpful aggravation from the North Pole but got some relief from the South Pole on the following day. Although a faithful follower of homeopathy, Lord Elgin does not seem to have done its cause much good – the disposition of his symptoms to aggravate under treatment attracted attention, and a contemporary memoir notes how he was in constant pain due to the action of homeopathic remedies!

Mme Leloir, the early stages of whose case we have already looked at (see pages 54–6), was another frequent visitor on whom Hahnemann had the opportunity to try out a number of remedies. When she had consulted the Hahnemanns early in their time in Paris she complained of digestive problems. Under treatment, it seems that an old suppressed condition gradually began to re-establish itself, in which her gullet, eyelids and fingers became paralysed for differing lengths of time. Sometimes she could not lift things, sometimes she could not talk because she lost the use of her tongue, frequently she had difficulty in swallowing.

Hahnemann gave Sulphur of course, intermittently, but also prescribed Arnica, Phosphoric Acid, Mercurius Sublimatus, Phosphorus, Cinnabar, Carbo Animalis, Antimonium Crudum and Oleander in succession. He also tried Laurocerasus. He prescribed Arnica with some success after repertorising the single symptom of 'paralysis', which yielded: 'Caust, kali phos, stannum, sulphur, ambra, arnica, colchicum, lachesis, laurocerasus, oleand, plumbum, pall, ruta.'

Wherever possible, Hahnemann sought confirming characteristic symptoms, so, for example, when he prescribed Oleander to the same patient, he did so on the confirmatory symptom of 'frequent eructations ameliorate: Oleand, natrum mur'. He later prescribed Phosphoric Acid on the more particularising symptom of 'opening of the eyelids' and 'belching of air in the night', and also on the symptom of 'her ear often hurts while eating'. Alumina was prescribed when, in addition to her apparent paralytic symptoms, Mme Leloir disclosed that her stool, always difficult, was now like sheep-droppings.

Of course these remedies had other applications. They were not confined to use in this area of 'nervous' complaints whose general characteristics most clearly matched the generals of the remedies. Hahnemann would frequently use them in quite other conditions where a characteristic symptom gave him the clue to do so.

Yet other commonly used remedies reflect the sycotic patterns laid down by gonorrhoea. Hahnemann was already beginning to use Thuja in situations where there was a more generalised sycotic picture than the mere presence of gonorrhoea. He often succeeded with it where Cinnabar had seemed indicated but was not completely effective. For example, Mme Bournichon, whose symptoms had improved only a little on Cinnabar, improved hugely on a long sequence of prescriptions of Thuja, and she remained well for several months. M. Dupont, who had a black spot in front of his eye, had been treated with Cinnabar and Nitric Acid without effect, but improved considerably in himself after Thuja (although the black spot got bigger).

Other 'sycotic' remedies displayed the well-known symptoms affecting the urinary tract: Agnus Castus, Cannabis Sativa, Cantharis,

Clematis, Copaiva, Petroselinum, Sarsaparilla and Selenium. Many patients had problems of this kind and were treated with a sequence of appropriate remedies. We have already met Mr Lyster, who had long-standing problems arising from a venereal disease suppressed by mercury. He suffered from attacks of gout which were normally presaged by gonorrhoeal discharges. Hahnemann customarily treated the discharge phase of the attack with a number of different remedies, including Clematis and Selenium.

There were many other patients in a similar state. M. Rauert was treated with Cannabis, Thuja and Selenium for his recurrent gonorrhoeal discharge. Mr Charles French, a 29-year-old English teacher, had a fissure in the urethra which had been cauterised. He also had a history of gonorrhoea. He had had hydrotherapy, leeches and various medications. He was prescribed Selenium and Clematis. Lady Elgin was given Petroselinum when she was suffering from burning urine, and M. Framin was successfully prescribed Agnus Castus.

Although such remedies were commonly prescribed for conditions affecting the genito-urinary system, it would be a mistake to think that their use was entirely restricted to such conditions. Selenium, for instance, was used in toothache, while Cannabis was frequently effective in respiratory affections. Sarsaparilla was used in cases of rheumatism.

Rheumatism, arthritis and gout were common after-effects of venereal disease and remedies with affinities to joints and muscles were therefore constantly called upon. Chief among these were: Bryonia, Causticum, Colocynthis, Conium, Guaiacum, Platina, Spigelia, Rhus Tox. and Ruta. Other remedies were also needed though less frequently: Antimonium Crudum, Aurum Metallicum, Camphor, Clematis, Colchicum, Dulcamara, Ledum Palustre, Manganum, Oleander, Saponinum and Senega.

The sculptor M. Auguste was given a succession of such remedies. Hahnemann opened with Hepar Sulph. and then proceeded to prescribe remedies more specifically related to his condition, including Sepia, Platina, Causticum and Rhus Tox., until he gradually improved. Once more Mr Lyster's case provides us with numerous examples of the use of such remedies. He had gout and amaurosis as a consequence of syphilis and its treatments, and was given a succession of remedies including Guaiacum, Strontium, Cannabis, Conium, Lachesis, Ruta, Colchicum, Spigelia, Oleander, Selenium, Cinnabar, Thuja and Calcarea Carbonica. General Baudraud, aged 68 when he first came, had gout worse for walking and for riding at faster than walking pace.

He had benefited from allopathic colchicum and taken other allopathic remedies. Hahnemann treated him basically with Sulphur, Rhus Tox. and sac lac and an occasional dose of Aconite whenever the pain was acute and severe. In the later stages he occasionally gave him Staphysagria, Causticum and Rhododendron.

Once again we must be clear that, although these general states might be those which most commonly called for such remedies, the remedies would be used in quite other conditions if the symptoms agreed. So for instance, as we have seen earlier, Mme Leloir had a pain in her kidneys which improved on Rhus Tox. It was a right-sided pain, better lying on the left side. It improved if she walked about for part of the night. After taking Rhus Tox. for a while she developed an erysipelatous eruption with a burning face, but felt very well in herself with a general amelioration of symptoms.

Respiratory complaints were extremely common among Hahnemann's patients, and even in the absence of what might be called firm diagnoses it is clear that these had become increasingly prevalent. There is scarcely a single patient who does not have problems to do with throat, chest or lungs. These complaints ranged from the sore throats and strained vocal chords of the many actors and singers among the patients, through asthma and bronchitis to florid phthisis (or consumption), as that disease took a stronger hold on the community (in Hahnemann's time it had not yet reached its peak).

Phthisis and the related scrofula are now regarded as separate diseases, the former deriving from infection by *Mycobacterium tuberculosis* and the latter from infection by *Mycobacterium bovis*. The entry point for the former is normally through the respiratory tract, for the latter through the alimentary tract. Scrofula, once called the King's Evil, was characterised by swellings of the lymph nodes or glands, which seemed to distinguish it from phthisis with its cough, fever and emaciation. However scrofulous children were observed often to develop tuberculosis, and autopsies sometimes revealed that patients with phthisis had extensive swelling of the lymph glands, so there was assumed to be a relationship between the two conditions. Diseases that we call cancer were also included in the definition of phthisis at this time. The swollen glands, difficult respiration, bloody sputum and eventual death which was the common fate of consumptive patients are often met with in these casebooks, and often in patients with a scrofulous history (scrofula was normally a disease of childhood).

A variety of remedies was called upon to treat patients with such conditions. Common were: Ammonium Carbonicum, Ammonium

Muriaticum, Arsenicum Album, Bryonia Alba, Camphora, Cannabis, Capsicum, Causticum, Drosera, Dulcamara, Ipecacuanha, Lycopodium Clavatum, Mercurius Solubilis, Phosphorus, Rhus Tox., Spongia Tosta and Stannum.

Newer remedies were tried occasionally, often in otherwise hopeless cases: Auto, Isopath, Orpiment (Auripigmentum), Oxymuriatic Acid, Ozaena and Phellandrium. Psoricum was given once; Ranunculus Bulbosus and Ranunculus Sceleratus were both used occasionally, as were Rhododendron, Squilla, Sulphuric Acid and Verbascum.

Mlle St. Ouen was given Arsenicum, Lycopodium and Stannum in succession for her chronic chest condition. After the Stannum she developed a great sensitivity in the chest. She felt better, had little expectoration and cough, but still had a little fever at night. After Orpiment 30c she was much better, to Hahnemann's surprise (he put '!!!' in the margin). Her fever, expectoration and sensitivity of the chest all diminished. Hahnemann continued to prescribe Orpiment in the 24th potency and she continued to make good progress until she developed a fever, whereupon he administered Aconite until the fever subsided, followed by Causticum, prescribed when his patient mentioned that she coughed much more while talking. Causticum improved the cough a little.

M. Lecointe was an engaging young man about town who had clearly succumbed to phthisis. He was prescribed Hepar Sulph. for a long time, then Causticum, then China. He was much improved after China for a while, but then flagged and developed a corneal ulcer. Hahnemann turned to Isopath twice daily, which effected a temporary improvement. He also used Oxymuriatic Acid 30c, sac lac and Phosphorus. There was some improvement and Hahnemann reverted to the use of Isopath in several different potencies. M. Lecointe continued to improve, but eventually stopped coming while still incompletely cured.

Looking at the remedies in this way brings into focus the relationship between phthisis and syphilis, because we see repeatedly a relation between those remedies which are indicated in mercurial or syphilitic affections and those which are indicated in phthisis. The tubercular miasm can be seen clearly emerging.

Mme LELOIR
(continuation)

Towards the end of November 1839 Mme Leloir returned after a long gap in treatment. She had now developed different symptoms; intermittent paralysis of various muscles, especially throat and fingers. We pick up the text in May 1840 after Hahnemann had tackled the new symptom picture largely with Sulphur (with an interlude for treatment of an acute sore throat with Causticum and Belladonna).

Casebook entry: **2**/209 (see facsimile, overleaf)

May 19th [1840]
Headache lasted till the 15th, the same length of time as the colic. On the 16th had less colic; 17th sensation of weakness. 2 fingers paralysed. For 2 days difficulty in drinking and speaking. She speaks nasally. Dry cough. Cannot expectorate. No more blood in the stools.
This morning a very small white hard stool. The 14th a little diarrhoea. Since yesterday some appetite. Yesterday lancinating pains in the back. A lot of wind. Always icy feet. Always a little dry cough. For two days leucorrhoea without any sensation. Sometimes her throat is constricted. Out of breath on ascending. For several days has often had a desire to urinate a little (along with desire to pass a stool). While she is lying down she has no desire to urinate and her two fingers are not paralysed!

Repertory
(G) *Better for eructations: oleand, (arn, spong) Lyc, nat m*
(G) *Fruitless desire for stool: Nat m, Sulph, Oleand, Nux v*

Prescription
Sulphur 197c (. /197/100) 1 drop in 7 [tablespoonfuls of water and] ½ [of alcohol]. One tablespoonful in a glass of water and take one teaspoonful [daily].

May 27th [1840]
(Period May 27th=24 days). Hands are constricted. 23/24 had a kind of paralysis of mouth, tongue, pharynx and speech which lasted for less than a minute while she was dining. Her throat closed up and she could not swallow much liquid or food at the same time. This has lasted for 15 days. When she coughs she feels there is mucus which she cannot expectorate. Very thick sticky saliva. Heaviness in the right

Mme Leloir: Samuel's habit of asking supplementary questions after Melanie had taken things down in the words of the patient is clearly illustrated. There are further examples of repertorisation and the introduction of new notations – the subscript 100 and the + symbol. Note the absence of any indication of potency for Laurocerasus.

arm. She is speaking nasally. Sometimes when she has talked too much it tires her to speak even a little. *Breaks wind all the time, even at night. During her periods she can have a stool without an enema. A few white spots still on the right tonsil.*

Repertory
(G) *Speech impediment caused by stroke: Laur*

Prescription
Laurocerasus (potency not specified) in 10 [tablespoonfuls of water and half of alcohol]. Put 1 tablespoonful in a glass and take 1 teaspoonful [from that daily].

June 11th [1840]
Yesterday morning she had the last small spoonful. She is eating straw-berries and can therefore have a stool everyday. Her right arm has become very much heavier. She has great difficulty in writing as she has less power again in the three fingers: thumb, index and middle. A great deal of difficulty in talking: larynx and tongue. She talks nasally. Always difficult to expectorate after coughing, which makes her retch. She can never swallow while eating. On rising in the morning she can still for a little while use her arm and hand. Her lower lip is drooping more and her breathing is faster. A lot of leucorrhoea. Still itching in both ears.

Repertory
(F) *Very frequent eructations relieve: oleand, nat m.*

Prescription
Oleander 30c (./X) 1 drop in 7 [tablespoonfuls of water and] ½[of alcohol]. Put 1 tablespoonful in a glass of water and from that take 1–2 teaspoonfuls [daily].

June 26th [1840]
Better. She still has a sensation of paralysis in the right hand and the right side of the throat but it is less. She is coughing a lot and has great difficulty expectorating. She cannot really spit. When she does so she brings up pus.

It is more difficult for her to speak when she has not broken wind. A stool every day. A lot of leucorrhoea.

Her right index finger is today half paralysed for the first time. She has a few pains in the right side of the throat when she swallows, especially at the back.

Prescription
Sulphur 20c+ (. /20+) in 7 [tablespoonfuls of water and] ½ [of alcohol]. Put 1 tablespoonful in a glass of water and from that take 1–3 teaspoonfuls [daily].

page **2**/210

July 1st [1840]
(Period 22 June)
Temporary paralysis of upper left eyelid – before taking the Sulphur 20c+ whenever this paralysis manifested the right eye opened freely. It lasted for two days.

Sometimes speaks through her nose. Her throat is getting better but there are still a few spots.

Repertory
(F) Upper eyelid opens with difficulty: acon, cham, cocc, Hyosc.
(G) Closing of eyelid: cham, Hyosc, stram.
(G) Closing; Ars, nat m, Bell, Phos, Sep, Merc.

Index finger is good; there is weakness in the right wrist. Coughing a lot, difficult expectoration, yellow sputum. One stool every day. Leucorrhoea and pains in the stomach. Very little appetite.

Prescription
Sulphur 21c+ (. /21+), 1 drop in 7 [tablespoonfuls decanted] into 2 glasses of water.

July 8th [1840]
Continuous wind upwards. State of the throat the same ... Paralytic affection of left eye the same. Great difficulty in expectorating. Immediately after eating she gets hoarse. She speaks better after breaking wind. Her left hand is less swollen. On the 5th, 6th, 7th, hoarseness. While dining she felt her tongue paralysing for a quarter of an hour and she could not eat any more.

She is coughing less; spat a little pus. Not too much saliva. She has been going to stool with more difficulty. A lot of leucorrhoea. Better

appetite. Gums bleeding in the morning. Sometimes she's reluctant to swallow; it's as if her tongue is paralysed.
Every day she breaks wind.

Repertory
(F) *(Tongue as if paralysed: Caus, Dulc, Nux m)*

Prescription
Sulphur 22c+ (. /22+) in 7 [tablespoonfuls] and 2 glasses, take 1–2 teaspoonfuls [daily].

She was much improved after this prescription.

NOTES

1. Hahnemann was not entirely original in this. Several of his contemporaries had distinguished between syphilis and what was called sycosis (fig disease): the distinction was 'in the air'. The idea that it was dangerous to suppress an eruption was also part of the humoral tradition of medicine. What Hahnemann did was develop the idea and apply it across a whole range of illnesses.
2. Jahr's surprise that Hahnemann did not appreciate the ravages of venereal disease is expressed in his book, *The Venereal Diseases*, trans. C. J. Hempel, New York 1868, p. vi.
3. G. H. G. Jahr, *New Manual*, trans. J. Laurie, London 1841.
4. In Vol. 2 of the casebooks Hahnemann occasionally prescribed Hepar Sulph. Weber. Presumably this means that he was prescribing Hepar Sulph. potentised according to the method of George Weber, a Parisian pharmacist and homeopath. Weber's preparations were all (soluble or not) taken to the fifteenth potency by trituration before there was any dilution. (See Weber, G., *Codex des médicaments homoéopathiques*, Paris 1854, p. 52.)
   Hahnemann also occasionally prescribed a remedy called Hepar Sulph. Natronatum, a name for a 'trisulfure de sodium impur' according to a personal communication from Dr Jacques Baur, who notes that T. L. Bradford wrongly identified Hepar Sulph. Natronatum with Natrum Sulphuricum, the latter being a sulphate and not a sulphur.
5. J. H. Clarke, *A Dictionary of Practical Materia Medica*, London 1900.
6. *ibid.*

Chapter 7

Iatrogenic Disease

According to Hahnemann, the third most important cause of widespread chronic disease after psora, then syphilis and sycosis, was medical treatment itself, and this is certainly clearly demonstrated in the casebooks, though he was hardly able to counter its effects by the use of specific remedies. Hahnemann in fact considered diseases which had been compounded by allopathic treatment to be incurable.[1] Yet the bulk of his practice in Paris consisted of people who had not only had a considerable amount of allopathic treatment already, but had often manifestly been damaged by it. His task was thus almost impossible from the outset. Studying these cases we become acutely aware of the circumstances which made him realise the harm being done by the excesses of orthodox medical treatment, in particular the extensive use of toxic drugs and the even more widespread practice of bloodletting, whether surgically or by the application of leeches.

DRUG EFFECTS

The previous medical treatment to which patients had been subjected may have varied in its nature, but it was uniformly horrific in its effects. The widespread use of mercury was, of course, a major source of the iatrogenic illness exposed in these records. It was used as a cure for many different kinds of illness, notably for the rampant venereal disease. It was the only remedy known to be effective against venereal disease throughout the eighteenth and nineteenth centuries. The treatment, whether for syphilis or gonorrhoea, was usually mercury or a mercury compound such as calomel, given in doses strong enough to make the patient salivate. The common side effects, observed countless times in Hahnemann's patients, were ulcers, falling-out of teeth, caries of the bones, trembling, paralysis and various 'nervous' conditions. Although the toxic effects of mercury were well understood, they were regarded as preferable to the symptoms of the disease they were

109

used to control; it had much the same position as the modern power-ful anti-cancer agents. In the 1840s allopathic potassium iodide was introduced as a new specific.[2]

Mercury was in fact the chief anti-inflammatory agent used in orthodox medicine at this time, regardless of the cause of the inflam-mation, and it was prescribed extensively, not only to patients iden-tified as having venereal disease. It was commonly used to treat any severe skin disease and was used both externally and internally. Externally, mercury ointments or rubs were used; sometimes mercury baths, which were generally thought to be milder. Internally it was given in liquid form, in syrups, for example Syrup van Swieten and Syrup de Gibert. It was also given internally in the form of calomel, which gradually took over from pure mercury as a cure-all as the nineteenth century progressed. Calomel ointment was used for itching of diverse origins and calomel was also used internally for infantile cholera, chronic diarrhoea, dysentery and typhoid. Pure mercury con-tinued in frequent use internally as a purgative.

Many patients had suffered and were still suffering from the widespread use of this powerful drug. M. Sy, the leading bassoonist in Musard's orchestra, had suffered from exostoses in all his joints since being treated with mercury for venereal disease. Mme de St. Cloud suffered from numerous physical symptoms, palpitations and nightmares caused by her nerves having been attacked by the mercury from purgatives and mercury baths. Vicomtesse Beugnot suffered as much from the calomel with which her malarial fever had been treated as she did from her grief at the loss of a child, Hahnemann noted as he took her case. Mme Dumas had used a lot of mercury both internally and externally to counter the venereal disease acquired from her husband. Because of this she had developed a 'mercurial disease'. Paganini had had mercury rubs for five months; these had caused constipation, destroyed his teeth and spoilt his eyes.

In addition to mercury, Hahnemann singled out other contemporary drugs for censure: silver nitrate, used as a diuretic, iodine, opium – a sedative of the highest order, valerian, frequently used as a sleeping draught; cinchona bark (or quinine), the wonder drug of the eighteenth century and practically a specific for the widespread malaria. The effects of cinchona or quinine poisoning were in turn often treated by arsenic, which brought about its own undesirable effects. Foxglove (digitalis) had proved effective in controlling certain forms of heart disease, particularly those resulting in dropsy. However, its overuse was rife. Hahnemann also specifically condemned prussic acid, sulphur and sulphuric acid.[3] He might have added dozens of other names such as belladonna, bertaluf, copaiva, kimini, morphine and sarsaparilla, to name but a few. Such were the contemporary equivalents of our antibiotics, cortisone tablets and ointments, inhalers, tranquillisers and antidepressants. It is obvious from their names that Hahnemann was not slow to marshal these medicines into the service of homeopathy.

Patients occasionally made explicit the fact that such drugs had caused damage. For instance, M. Auguste was sure his joint and bone pains had been worse since he had had foot baths in iodum; M. Rougier was clear that he had suffered from the action of digitalis; Paganini that some of his ailments had been caused by morphine. At other times their effects, so familiar, pass without individual comment.

In fact, the active use of heavy doses of such drugs had diminished to some extent in Paris itself by the time Hahnemann arrived there. Where patients have had really 'heroic' drug treatment it had often been administered abroad, for the Paris of the early nineteenth century was in many respects the most medically enlightened city in Europe.[4] The French Revolution had swept away many of the old doctrines and prejudices in the treatment of illness, and for a while there had been a vogue for the use of diet, exercise and hydrotherapy instead of heavy doses of drugs. Where this was not the case, doctors were at least prescribing on the simpler basis of 'Brunonism', the influential theory of John Brown.

In the late eighteenth century in Scotland, William Cullen had founded a medical system on the assumption that the basic phenomenon of life and disease was a 'nervous force'. His pupil John Brown had gone on from this to develop the notion that all disease was either 'sthenic' or 'asthenic', due to excess or defect of nature's stimulation, and that correction of disease merely required a balanced adjustment of such stimulation: the patient needed merely either to be sedated or further stimulated. Sthenic diseases called for sedation by opium, other sedatives or bloodletting, asthenic diseases for stimulation by huge doses of gamboge, aconite, ipecacuanha or nux vomica and other such drugs in their crude form. Brown's system prevailed over much of Europe, and though heavy doses of drugs were still used, the simplification of the combinations was seen by Hahnemann as a step in the right direction. At least initially, Hahnemann's response to Brunonism was quite benevolent.[5]

BLOODLETTING

Far more dangerous, and more prominent in the symptom pictures of Hahnemann's patients, were the effects of one of the treatments which had replaced the use of heroic doses of drugs: bloodletting. Blood-letting had always been a treatment favoured by the medical profession. Originally it had been an integral part of the Galenic theory of humours, the predominant medical theory for many centuries. According to this there were four fluids or humours in the body: blood, phlegm, black bile and yellow bile. Imbalance in these was what made people ill. To make them well it was merely necessary to restore balance by drawing off the blood in which a particular humour resided – at least, so went the theory. Even when advances in the science of dissection embarrassingly failed to reveal the presence of such humours in the body, the practice of bleeding remained popular and its function was merely redefined. Since it was a skill which doctors had acquired it was necessary to preserve a role for it.

In Hahnemann's day in Paris it was considered to be important as a technique for relieving inflammation. Inflammation could be derived or diverted from any site at which it had become established, by the letting of blood. This was done either by venesection, surgically opening a vein, or by the more drastic arteriosection, opening an artery. Other less life-threatening methods were the use of cauterisation, vesicatories (little suction cups applied to the skin), setons (resined horse-hair inserted into the skin on a needle and left there to set up a site of inflammation, and blisters, all of which were used to establish an alternative site of inflammation in the body and hence to derive or draw inflammation away from the infected part.

Hahnemann had attacked this practice all his life, but the extent to which it was used in France must have seemed like his worst nightmare. He arrived in Paris in the heyday of the notorious Jean-François Broussais, quite the most charismatic doctor of his time. Broussais had determined, and persuaded most of the doctors in Paris of his rightness, that all illness arose from gastric inflammation and that the only effective treatment was a combination of diet and bleeding. In place of the surgical drawing of blood, he advocated the direct application of leeches to the body as being the quickest and most effective form of letting blood and thereby gained a reputation for having spilt more of the vital fluid than Napoleon. In a period of four years, the balance of France's leech trade swung from an annual export of one million to an annual import of four. As Hahnemann pointed out, this was a good thing for homeopathy because the apothecaries, who had so opposed him in Germany when their profits were hit by his minimalist prescribing, had already lost all their power in Paris on account of Broussais. This fact did little to endear Broussais to Hahnemann, however, and he fulminated against him vigorously: 'Of all therapies ever conceived there is none more allopathic, senseless and futile than Broussais' debilitating bloodletting and starvation diet, which have been widespread for years. No sensible man could ever find any medical benefit in such treatment, whereas a real medicinal substance, even arbitrarily chosen, has now and then helped a patient because it happened to be homeopathic. But what can common sense expect from bloodletting other than the certain impairment and short-ening of life?'[6]

The common contemporary medical use of bleeding and venesection for a variety of illnesses had brought about its own clear disease pattern. Long-lasting weakness followed venesection, and infected swellings followed leeching. M. Cotran's sight had been affected when leeches were applied to his temples in an attempt to cure his headaches. So had M. Rousselot's. Mme Chueleher had been ill and unable to walk since leeching and cupping six months previously. She had been bled 'enormously'. M. Paul Brodgi had been weak and ill since a bleeding. Mme Laplace had been ill since being bled at home by her husband! The violinist M. Max Böhrer had been treated for the cramps in his fingers with vesicatories and still had them on his thigh when he visited the Hahnemanns in 1839: 'He has had vesicatories since 1826, first on the left arm, then on the right. At present he has them on the left thigh . . . In Berlin in 1825 and 1826 he had oozing scabs on the tips of his fingers which were treated with vesicatories and lead ointment . . . Two years ago he closed the vesicatories and suffered from breathlessness. Before the vesicatories were applied he had been terrified of dying whenever he had to touch a living being, man or dog.'

Mme Baudraud was 'fatigued by bleeding, cauterisation, vesica-tories, and pastelles of talc'. Mme de Dampière had had erysipelas caused by leeches. Mme Deville's reaction was particularly long-lasting. She had had a painful swelling of the left arm with numbness since twelve leeches had been applied to it six months previously. It took even Hahnemann two years to bring it back to normal.

113

WOMEN'S PROBLEMS

Whatever the allopathic treatment, it was, then as now, women who were particularly liable to be adversely affected by it because, on the whole, as a result of the increasing medicalisation of childbearing, they were more subject to it. Although in many cases the manifold pains and multiform symptoms which women reported were due to unrecognised venereal disease, in many others the problems were undoubtedly due to the effects of medical treatment. The gross effects of badly handled confinement, labour and birth were all too common. The problems caused by hormonal imbalances and excessive menstrual bleeding were compounded by the medical treatment of leeching for these conditions. In consequence, what looks like anaemia seems to have been rife. Its symptoms of weakness, tiredness and depression are often reported, though the condition was not explicitly diagnosed. Excessive childbearing and the persistent use of laxatives compounded this state. We see numerous exhausted and depleted women coming to consult Hahnemann.

Many of the apparent cases of 'nerves' and alleged 'hysteria' were probably due to such exhaustion and depletion.[7] Hahnemann frequently dealt with cases of 'nerves' of diverse origin, whether related to the effects of mercurial poisoning, as in the case of Mme de St. Cloud, or to the effects of gynaecological problems or grief or disappointment, as was very commonly the case. Such states commonly involved attacks of nerves, fainting, palpitations, weakness and neuralgia.

Many women had acquired a septic condition at the time of childbirth from which they never fully recovered. Mme de St. Cloud had been ill for this reason since her only pregnancy three and a half years earlier. Lady Belfast had been ill for eight years and had seen sixteen doctors since the birth of her last child. Lady Kinnaird's bad health dated from incompetent medical treatment after the birth of a child. Mme Michelon had sustained lasting physical damage after her child had been delivered by a 'man without experience'. Nine years later she was still suffering.

In the pages of the casebooks we can watch Hahnemann developing an armamentorium of remedies to deal with conditions specific, or almost so, to the ailments characteristic of women. Naturally he frequently had recourse to remedies such as China, Ferrum Metallicum, Ignatia, Lachesis, Pulsatilla and Sepia. However, he also drew inventively on other, newer and less well-proved remedies in order to bring some relief to his women patients, including Asarum, Cocculus, Coffea, Crotalus Horridus, Iodum, Kreosotum, Melilotus, Murex Purpurea, Oleander, Ratanhia, Sabina, Secale Cornutum, Staphysagria. Even newer remedies were also tried out: Crocus Sativa, Gratiola, Laurocerasus, Moschus, Nux Moschata and Nitri Spiritus Dulcis, for instance.

The cases of women such as Mrs Boddington, Mme de St. Cloud, Mrs Erskine, Mme Figuera, Mme Giffrier, Mme Gueroult, Mme Lamartinière and Miss Stirling all exemplify the confusion and combination of these symptoms.

Mme Gueroult, whose health was described as 'delicate', had a series of remedies including Carbo Animalis, Cinnabar, Nux Moschata, Calcarea Carbonica, Camphor, Platina, Ambra Grisea, Natrum Carbonicum, Strontium, Pulsatilla, Zincum, Natrum Muriaticum, Alumina, Nux Vomica, Phosphorus and Drosera.

Mme Figuera had had trouble with nerves at the time of menstruation ever since her periods had begun at the age of thirteen and been suppressed for three months by cold bathing. She was severely mentally disturbed for six months after her first pregnancy: this condition had been cured by cold bathing. Hahnemann began with Sulphur, prescribing it in ascending LM potencies for six weeks and then moving on to Sabina, Hepar Sulph. and Mercurius Dulcis. All the old symptoms then returned and Cocculus was prescribed for two weeks, Hahnemann wondering whether the return of symptoms could have been the effect of the Sabina. After some stability had been restored, and Mme Figuera reported suffering only from itching in the sexual parts and abdominal wind, he prescribed Hepar Su'ɔh. This did little for the wind and Carbo Animalis was then prescribed for some time and with some success. Once again the periods became the focus of the prescribing and Kali Carbonicum was given, followed in succession by Crocus, Ferrum, Secale Cornutum, Belladonna, Cinnabar, Ignatia, Cicuta, Antimonium Crudum and Lycopodium. The remedies were prescribed at every slight change of symptoms until Lycopodium finally took hold and it alone was prescribed for some time, then Cinnabar was used for a while, followed by Calcarea Carbonica. Then Laurocerasus, Magnesium Muriaticum and, finally, Tabacum all participated in the cure.

Mme Lamartinière's whole body was sensitive to external touch. She suffered from a continuous tearing pain in the head. The headache was such that a fly walking across her forehead could make her ill. Hahnemann prescribed Asarum. Not only was her headache completely better but all other symptoms improved on Asarum, as he wrote in the notes.

VACCINATION

Adverse effects from smallpox vaccination were sometimes reported. These were usually in the form of stubborn pustules or pox which would not go away. Mme Moreau and Mrs Lennox both needed treatment for these, and many patients reported lesser scabs and pustules which dated from a vaccination. (M. Duchine had been ill since having smallpox itself.) Mme Moreau's case is particularly interesting as it illustrates the orthodox use of mercury and leeching in an attempt to cure the eruptions caused by the vaccination.

'At the age of twenty-five she was vaccinated for the second time from the arm of a child covered with pustules and since then she has had pustules on her face. A mercurial ointment has been applied. Eight leeches have been applied to her thighs three times a year ... At the age of twenty-six she lost all her teeth.'

Hahnemann treated her succesfully, though over a period of months, with successive doses of Sulphur in the LM potency and sac lac (see pages 47–53).

HYDROTHERAPY

Not all contemporary allopathic treatment seems to have been equally dangerous. Hydrotherapy, of course, was fashionable at this time. Most patients had visited spas and taken the waters at some time, either the many French ones, especially those of Auteuil, Vichy and Enghien, near to Paris, or the internationally renowned ones such as Baden-Baden and Carlsbad. Hahnemann himself entertained mixed feelings about the effects of hydrotherapy. At one point he had been an enthusiastic advocate of it; later he had asserted that it was only useful when the nature of the water made it accidentally homeopathic to the patient's case. His patients' responses were also mixed.

Mme Grisenoi had taken the waters on the Rhone and in Rome. The waters of Mont d'Or had helped the tuberculous M. Lecointe a great deal. Some had tried the newly fashionable sea-bathing, though this was still regarded with some suspicion. Mme Figuera felt much better for her sea-bathing, but Mme Roquin felt that her condition had been aggravated by it. M. Springsfeld of Aachen suffered from a kind of imbecility which came on after a grave illness in 1831. Hahnemann seems to have been very suspicious of the fact that he had been in the habit of taking cold baths at Aachen and Burtscheid. His health had started to deteriorate in 1824, had become drastically worse after an accident in 1831 and irretrievably bad after a loss of fortune in 1837 'which shocked him terribly and brought on the symptoms of nervous apoplexy.' The musician M. Rousselot, who suffered from a severe form of vertigo that sounds like Menière's disease, had had previous homeopathic treatment and had remained well after this until he went sea-bathing, and it was then that his attacks had returned.

ELECTROTHERAPY AND MAGNETISM

Another type of medical treatment then in vogue was the therapeutic use of electricity, another process of which Hahnemann had once spoken with positive approval.[8] This was no new fad: numerous experiments relative to the medical application of electricity had been undertaken since the mid-eighteenth century with some success.[9] It had early been discovered that electric shocks could stimulate muscle and be of assistance in cases of paralysis. As early as the 1760s in England, John Wesley had promoted the medical use of electricity as part of his campaign against expensive medicine and compound drugs. He procured a machine and began to cure hundreds around the country in conjunction with his preaching. Other non-medical practitioners had done the same and, as the century progressed, more and more cures were reported, largely in cases of paralysis. There were, however, considerable limitations in the use of electricity, largely because of the difficulty of regulating the current at that time, and electrotherapy therefore remained on the margins of medicine.

Hahnemann himself was interested not only in the therapeutic use of electricity but also in the use of the related magnetism. His interest in this subject is apparent from the first edition of the *Organon*, where he used the example of magnetic attraction to describe the process of infection. In later editions he also used this analogy to explain the action of the vital force. Earlier scientists had thought that electricity and magnetism might be identical with the 'nervous fluid' which caused the nerves to be stimulated. Some thought that this nervous fluid was the same as the 'ether' which provided the missing link between the divine energy source (or the power of the planets according to the secular model) and human energy or action. This explanation would have aligned the 'nervous fluid' quite closely to Hahnemann's vital force. Hahnemann had also 'proved' the action of magnets and prescribed Magnet as a remedy to Lord Elgin, as already mentioned. Hahnemann's interest in electricity and magnetism is yet another example of his advanced thinking and insatiable curiosity which was undeterred by the unfashionableness of any topic.

Magnetism was definitely disapproved of at the time. Franz Anton Mesmer (1734–1815) was the main figure associated with its therapeutic use. In a doctoral thesis written in 1765 he had sought to show that the stars and planets acted on the human body in health and disease by means of an invisible fluid. Later he postulated that this 'fluid' had some connection with magnetism and electricity. He suggested that human bodies contained a magnetic fluid which made them sensitive to the motion of the planets, and that this magnetic fluid could be influenced curatively by passing magnets over the body. He found that he himself could cure people by conducting or channeling the magnetic influence. Later he discovered he could achieve the same results by the power of touch alone and abandoned the use of actual magnets. Orthodox physicians strenuously and successfully attempted to discredit him, accusing him of achieving some of his cures by the power of suggestion. (Apparently they thought minds easier to manipulate than magnetic fluid.)

The discreditation of Mesmer had cast a shadow over the development of electrotherapy as a whole for a time, but by the time Hahnemann arrived in Paris it was beginning to enjoy something of a revival. The increasing sophistication of electrical machines had made it possible for physicians to deliver a predictable, steady current and to repeat experiments, and there were by then several doctors of repute practising electrotherapy in the hospitals. In the first half of the nineteenth century, research into the use of electricity increased enormously: it became clearer and clearer that it could be valuable in stimulating dead nerves and was used increasingly in the treatment of paralysis. It is in such cases that Hahnemann's patients report its use. It does not seem to have produced ill effects. Mr Lyster had already had some electrical treatment before consulting Hahnemann, while M. Yermaloff continued to be treated with electricity during homeopathic treatment, apparently with Hahnemann's agreement.

It is clear that Hahnemann's main personal interest was in mesmerism, however. He directly advocated its use in *Chronic Diseases*, where he wrote that if from being given too many remedies a patient 'falls into such an irritated state that . . . no medicine acts' then 'there may be in use a calming mesmeric stroke made from the crown of the head . . . slowly down over the body.'[10] He went further in the final edition of the *Organon*, writing that 'This healing force ... is a marvellous, priceless gift of God to man ... This healing force acts in different ways: on the one hand it replaces vital force in various places where it is deficient; and on the other hand it drains off, reduces, and more equally distributes it where it has become so strongly concentrated in certain parts that it has caused and sustained vague nervous conditions.'[11]

Its effects on patients are sparsely recorded. Mme Morrisse had been successfully magnetised by her husband. Mme Besson reported that she had been magnetising one of her friends for a long time and that this had tired her out. Lieutenant Burroughs consulted Hahnemann for eighteen months with some improvement and then left to be magnetised by Chapelin. Hahnemann even appeared to prescribe daily magnetism for Miss Russell: one complete pass every morning, he recommended. On at least one occasion he performed this service himself for a patient – a certain M. Mauduit had a violent attack of nerves or epilepsy lasting three hours after having a fall on his head. Hahnemann made one swift magnetic pass over the man, spreading his hand out over his patient from forehead to navel and directing his attention towards his chest, which was very inflamed. He quickly settled down and Hahnemann repeated the pass about eight times, each time the symptoms returned, until eventually they passed completely.

It seems clear that although there were numerous different external morbid influences with which Hahnemann had to contend, as well as infection and miasm, the chief of these were the prevalent orthodox practices of bloodletting and drugging. These practices caused severe anaemia and an untold number of 'side effects' which were frequently more terrible than the original disease. Throughout the casebooks we see him picking his way through the maze of drug effects and symptoms induced by medical treatment, his task hardly easier than ours today.

NOTES

1. S. Hahnemann, *Organon*, 6th edn, paragraph 75.
2. Hahnemann had already proved this substance as Kali Iodatum.
3. S. Hahnemann, *Organon*, 6th edn, paragraph 74.
4. See E. Ackerknecht, *Medicine at the Paris Hospital, 1794–1848*, Baltimore 1967; J. E. Lesch, *Science and Medicine in France*, Harvard 1984.
5. The possible influence of Brunonism on Hahnemann has been discussed by H. J. Schwanitz, 'Homöopathie und Braunianismus 1795–1844': *Medizin in Geschichte und Kultur*, Vol. 15, Stuttgart 1983.
6. S. Hahnemann, *Organon*, 6th edn, paragraph 74a.
7. See Edward Shorter, *A History of Women's Bodies*, London 1984. Female nervous problems were thought to originate in the womb, hence 'hysteria,' male nervous problems in the hypochondrium or stomach, hence 'hypochondria.'
8. In the first edition of *Chronic Diseases*. However, he had grown more wary by the 3rd edition and wrote (trans. Tafel, p. 240): 'At the end of these directions for treating chronic diseases, I recommended, in the first edition, the lightest electric sparks as an adjuvant for quickening parts that have been for a long time paralyzed and without sensation, these to be used besides anti-psoric treatment. I am sorry for this advice and take it back, as experience has taught me that this prescription has nowhere been followed strictly, but that larger electric sparks have always been used to the detriment of patients.'
9. See M. Rowbottom and C. Susskind, *Electricity and Medicine: History of their Interaction*, San Francisco 1984, Chapters 1–4.
10. S. Hahnemann, *Chronic Diseases*, 3rd edn, (trans. Tafel, p. 219).
11. S. Hahnemann, *Organon*, 6th edn, paragraph 288.

Chapter 8

Experimentation with Dosage and Potency

So far I have avoided the question of dosage and potency as far as possible. The matter is complicated and it seemed better to discuss the rest of Hahnemann's prescribing style before venturing into the murky depths of posology.

By the time Hahnemann came to Paris he had considerably modified his previous practice with regard to dosage and potency; he had stopped prescribing in single dry doses repeated very infrequently (the way of prescribing advocated in the main text of the fifth edition of the *Organon*), and had begun to prescribe the centesimal potencies in liquid. Throughout the Paris period he prescribed his remedies in liquid doses repeated frequently, either every other day, daily, or several times a day. He also made considerable use of the method of olfaction, or inhaling of remedies.

His continual experimentation with dosage and potency throughout these casebooks gives us a fascinating insight into the process of thought involved in his development of his potencies. From a reading of the sixth edition of the *Organon* one might be forgiven for getting the impression that he moved effortlessly from the use of dry doses of remedies in the centesimal potency (sparingly repeated), to the development of the LM potency, with its complicated daily repetition of the remedy diluted in a series of glasses of water. It is clear from the casebooks, however, that this transition had begun much earlier. Even before the beginning of the Paris practice, Hahnemann had moved away from the single dry-dose method of prescribing he had advocated for so long, and was advancing tentatively and experimentally towards the introduction of the LM potency.[1]

At the turn of the nineteenth century, in the very earliest days of his practice, when he had first started to use medicines according to the Law of Similars, Hahnemann had concentrated on finding remedies capable of producing a symptom picture in a healthy person which would match that of the sick person. The dosage of the relevant remedy had not at first seemed of paramount importance and he had sometimes used quite crude, potentially toxic, doses of the appropriate medicine: prescriptions such as half a grain of opium, for instance, or half to a whole grain of quinine were common in his early years.[2] He soon found, however, that he had to administer the medicinal substance in a much lower dosage than was common in orthodox medical practice, since the remedy's capacity to imitate – and hence provoke or elicit – symptoms similar to those originating in the sick person could clearly put too much strain on the patient, if those symptoms were recreated too strongly. He therefore began to give smaller and smaller doses, experimenting to discover the smallest which would be effective.

Such doses, though tiny by orthodox standards, remained material for some time. Hahnemann first began to talk about dilution in 1801 in relation to a suggested cure for scarlet fever. He advised the internal use of one drop of the tincture of opium 'thoroughly mixed with 500 drops of very dilute spirits of wine', one drop of this in turn to be mixed with a further 500 drops of very dilute spirits of wine. To the consternation of his critics he commented: 'It is incredible how small doses of the active principle of the medicine acting upon the whole system when given in the suitable case will achieve their object.'[3]

Also in 1801, in an article 'On the Power of Small Doses of Medicine', he referred for the first time to the 'dynamic action of medicines'.[4] Having accepted the principle of dilution, he experimented for a long time with doses both dilute and crude, and the earliest German casebooks (from 1801 onwards) show him exploring the use of differing methods over a period of many years. Even when he began to adopt dilution itself as a regular process, he varied the dilutions, using many different ratios of substance to diluent.[5] By 1810, in the first edition of the *Organon*, he still appeared to have settled on no standard dilution or dosage, and merely urged the physician to give the chosen homeopathic remedy in just so small a dose as will overcome and destroy the existing disease without further ado.[6] He failed, however, to indicate in any way what that might be.

CENTESIMAL DILUTION

Gradually, he began to settle down to use what we now take to be the standard 'centesimal' dilution, where one drop of medicine was diluted in 99 drops of water or water and alcohol and succussed, then one drop of that was diluted in 99 drops of water and alcohol and succussed, and so on. Dilutions of various strengths or potencies would then be poured over powders, pellets or granules: these would be allowed to dry out and the remedy would then be administered in a dry dose.

Hahnemann made many attempts to refine this system. He experimented with varying numbers of succussions.[7] He also tried to establish an optimum potency for each drug. For instance, he suggested in his *Materia Medica Pura* that remedies should be employed in specific potencies, viz. Angustura 6c, Manganum Aceticum 24c, Capsicum 9c, Colocynthis 18c and 21c. Verbascum and Spongia in tincture.[8] This attempt is interesting – it anticipates some modern experiments which seem to show that what we now know to be dynamic remedies can be effective in some potencies and not in others.[9] Probably Hahnemann had become empirically aware of the varying actions of remedies in different potencies, though he was as yet unable to systematise his awareness. At a later date, however, he seems to have decided that it was impossible to establish an optimum potency for each remedy; at that time he tried to standardise the use of potencies, suggesting that the thirtieth centesimal of all remedies should be used at all times, so that homeopaths could compare their results.[10]

While continuing to experiment with the preparation of his remedies, he gradually evolved a relatively stable method of administering them; this process is chronicled in the early editions of the *Organon*. The practitioner was to give one dose of a remedy in the appropriate centesimal potency, and then wait till its action was completed before either repeating or changing the dose or the remedy. 'Every improvement in an acute or a chronic disease, however small it be, provided it is definitely progressive, is a condition which absolutely forbids any further administration of any medicine as long as it lasts.'[11]

This advice was followed and taught by many of the influential prescribers of the nineteenth century, and certainly by those whose practice has been the model for modern English-speaking homeopaths.

REPETITION

However, in 1833 and 1834 Hahnemann had already voiced his doubts about this method. He had come to the conclusion that the giving of a single dose brought about cure too slowly, and suggested that more frequent repetition would be more expeditious: '... the slowly progressive amelioration consequent on a very minute dose, whose selection has been accurately homeopathic ... sometimes accomplishes all the good the remedy in question is capable from its nature of performing in a given case, in periods of forty, fifty or a hundred days. This is, however, but rarely the case; and besides, it must be a matter of great importance to the physician as well as to the patient that were it possible, this period should be diminished to one half, one quarter, and even still less, so that a much more rapid cure might be obtained. And this may be very happily effected . . . if this minutest yet powerful dose of the best selected medicine be repeated at suitable intervals.'[12]

In his note to this paragraph he expanded further, remarking that a single dose was rarely effective: 'One such smallest dose of medicine in our highly potentised dynamisation is evidently insufficient to effect all the curative action that might be expected from that medicine, for it may unquestionably be requisite to administer several of them, in order that the Vital Force may be pathogenetically altered by them.'[13]

However, although Hahnemann had decided that it was necessary to repeat remedies frequently, he had long been aware that such repetition could cause the appearance of symptoms of the repeated remedy, something he wished to avoid where possible. Because of this, he initially suggested that any symptoms emerging as a result of repeating a remedy should be responded to with another remedy which would counteract them. So, for instance, he suggested that when Sulphur was repeated, Nux Vomica or Hepar Sulph. should be given to counteract the possible unwelcome response: 'We may consider it requisite, as far as we can calculate, to give eight, nine or ten doses of Tinct. Sulph. (at X)[14] it is yet more expedient in such cases, instead of giving them in uninterrupted succession, to interpose after every, or every second or third dose, a dose of another medicine, which in this case is next in point of homeopathic suitableness to Sulphur (usually Hepar Sulph.) and to allow this likewise to act before again commencing a course of three doses of Sulphur. But it not infrequently happens that the vital force refuses to permit several doses of Sulphur, even though they may be essential for the cure of the chronic malady and are given at the intervals mentioned above, to act quietly on itself; this refusal it reveals by some, though moderate, Sulphur symptoms, which it allows to appear in the patient during the treatment. In such cases it is sometimes advisable to administer a small dose of Nux Vomica X, allowing it to act for eight or ten days, in order to dispose the system again to allow succeeding doses of the Sulphur to act quietly and effectually upon it. In those cases for which it is adapted, Pulsatilla X is preferable.'[15]

However, he did not use this method for very long and had in fact already substantially abandoned it by 1835, in favour of the method described in the Preface to the second edition of Volume 3 of *Chronic Diseases*, written in 1834 (though not published till 1838). Here he advocated that the potentised remedy should be diluted in liquid and administered in a divided dose, a spoonful at a time: 'It is most useful, in diseases of any magnitude, to give to the patient the powerful homeopathic pellet or pellets only in solution, and this solution in divided doses. In this way we give the medicine dissolved in 7 to 20 tablespoonfuls of water without any addition, in acute and very acute diseases, every 6, 4 or 2 hours. Where the danger is urgent, even every hour or half hour, a tablespoonful at a time. With weak persons or children, only a small part of a tablespoonful (one or two teaspoonfuls or coffeespoonfuls) may be given as a dose.'[16]

In the Paris casebooks, for instance, when Mme Grisenoi had a cough she was prescribed Belladonna 30c diluted in 7 tablespoonfuls of water, one teaspoonful to be taken at a time until her cough stopped.

Hahnemann used this method of administering the remedy constantly in the early years of the Paris practice, in both acute and chronic cases. In chronic cases, where the liquid would need to be kept for some time, he added a little alcohol (or charcoal for those who could not take alcohol) as a preservative.[17] Mrs Erskine, for instance, was given one dose of Sulphur 30c diluted in 15 tablespoonfuls of water with charcoal, one teaspoonful to be taken every evening. Later, after her reaction to the repetition had been observed, Hahnemann modified the prescription: the remedy was to be taken only once every other evening, with sac lac on the intervening evening.

MULTIPLE DOSES

Throughout the early Paris casebooks Hahnemann used what we now call low potencies, potencies up to 30c, in the following descending scale and with this notation: X=30c; VIII=24c; VI=18c; IV=12c; II=6c; I=3c. Belladonna 30c was written Belladonna . /X, Belladonna 24c was written Belladonna . /VIII. The dot before the line seems to have meant that one drop of the indicated remedy in the potency shown was to be dissolved in the liquid.[18] At this point in his practice he normally used drops of liquid remedies. When he wrote in the *Organon* and *Chronic Diseases*, he commonly referred to his doses as drops or pellets. He does, however, occasionally refer to a powder in the casebooks.

Sometimes more than one drop was to be diluted in the liquid. Mr Urchart, for instance, who began treatment on the same day as Mrs Erskine, was prescribed two drops of Sulphur 30c, (written as . . /X) to be diluted in 15 [table]spoonfuls [of water] and one of brandy, one tablespoonful of the mixture to be drunk every evening. Mme Braun was prescribed two drops of Hepar Sulph. 30c (. . /X) in 15 tablespoonfuls of liquid and, subsequently, three doses of Cinnabar 30c (. . . /X) also in 15 tablespoonfuls of liquid. M. Vandenberg took Bryonia . . /VI followed by Bryonia . . . /VI.

In some cases this practice was carried to extraordinary lengths. In the case of Mr Robert Lyster, for example, after opening the prescribing with Cinnabar 30c (. /X), Hahnemann prescribed the following sequence of remedies: Ruta . . . /X, 1 to 8 doses daily, Ruta 24c (. . . . . /VIII) similary, Sulphur . . . . . /160 (?) half in the morning, half in the evening, Thuja . . . /VIII in the morning, Nitric Acid . /X, half in the morning, half in the evening, Sulphur . . /197, 1 to 8 doses daily, then Cinnabar . . . /VI, 1 to 8 doses daily. Later he prescribed Ruta 30c (. . . /X), followed by Ruta 24c (. . . . . /VIII) and a number of other remedies, all with the same careful specification of the required number of drops (see facsimile overleaf).

Mr Lyster was considered to be sensitive to remedies and it looks as if Hahnemann might have been trying to reduce any potential aggravation by this method of varying the dose. This seems curious in view of the fact that he certainly regarded his potencies as immaterial and dynamic at this period, and theoretically the amount of the dose should not have affected the dynamic action of the remedy. That, at least, is modern theory. On the other hand, French prescribers still vary the doses as well as the potencies, and probably all homeopaths have patients who insist that they need two tablets to get any effect from a remedy.[19]

Hahnemann rarely wrote out his instructions in full. He frequently abbreviated and, since he was writing for himself and not posterity, wrote what he understood but we may not. The exact method by which, and quantity in which, the remedy was to be taken is not, therefore, always clear.[20] However, though the detail in each individual case may sometimes be obscured by Hahnemann's shorthand, the general pattern is apparent.

For the first few years of the Paris practice, he regularly prescribed low centesimal potencies diluted in liquid to be taken in repeated divided doses, usually every day or every other day, often more frequently. The liquid was sometimes water and sometimes water and alcohol (usually brandy, sometimes rum). The full instruction is written out sufficiently often for us to be able to be sure of the norm, though not always of the specific variations.

The amount of liquid in which the dose was diluted varied: it might be 7, 8, 15 or 30 tablespoonfuls. Often this seems to have been decided on the basis of the number of times the patient might be expected to take the remedy before the next appointment. Usually a 7 or 8 tablespoonfuls prescription was followed by an appointment a week later, a 15 tablespoonfuls prescription by one a fortnight later, and so on. Sometimes, however, the amount of liquid appears to have been determined according to how weak a dilution Hahnemann wanted for a particular dose.[21]

RUBBING

Sometimes, when he considered the patients to be sensitive, Hahnemann advised them to rub the diluted remedy onto their skin: 'Where more especial care is necessary, only the half of [the liquid] may be given; half a spoonful of this mixture may also well be used for ... external rubbing.'[22]

We have already noted Mr Lyster's being instructed to do this. On the 29th November 1836, Mrs Erskine was likewise instructed to take one spoonful of a liquid made from one drop of Hepar Sulph. 12c (. /IV) dissolved in 200 drops of water every morning and to rub herself with the other half of the mixture. In December 1836, M. Auguste the sculptor, who suffered from rheumatism, tinnitus and bloody diarrhoea, was prescribed Hepar Sulph. 12c (. /IV) in 15 tablespoonfuls of water plus a little charcoal. He was to take one teaspoonful every other morning and to use one teaspoonful to rub himself.

This method of prescribing was used quite frequently in the first two years or so of the Paris practice, but was then substantially abandoned and used only on rare occasions. The external application of the remedy was to be made to a healthy area of skin, not to a lesion, and was seen as an alternative method of introducing a remedy into the body and not as a curative external application. As always, however, Hahnemann was prepared to break his own rules, and in the case of M. Chauchot he advised the application of potentised Ozaena to a polyp, while in the case of Mrs Boddington, who had advanced ulceration of the breast, he appears to have advised the application of potentised Arsenicum to the ulcerated part, but these were exceptions to his normal practice.

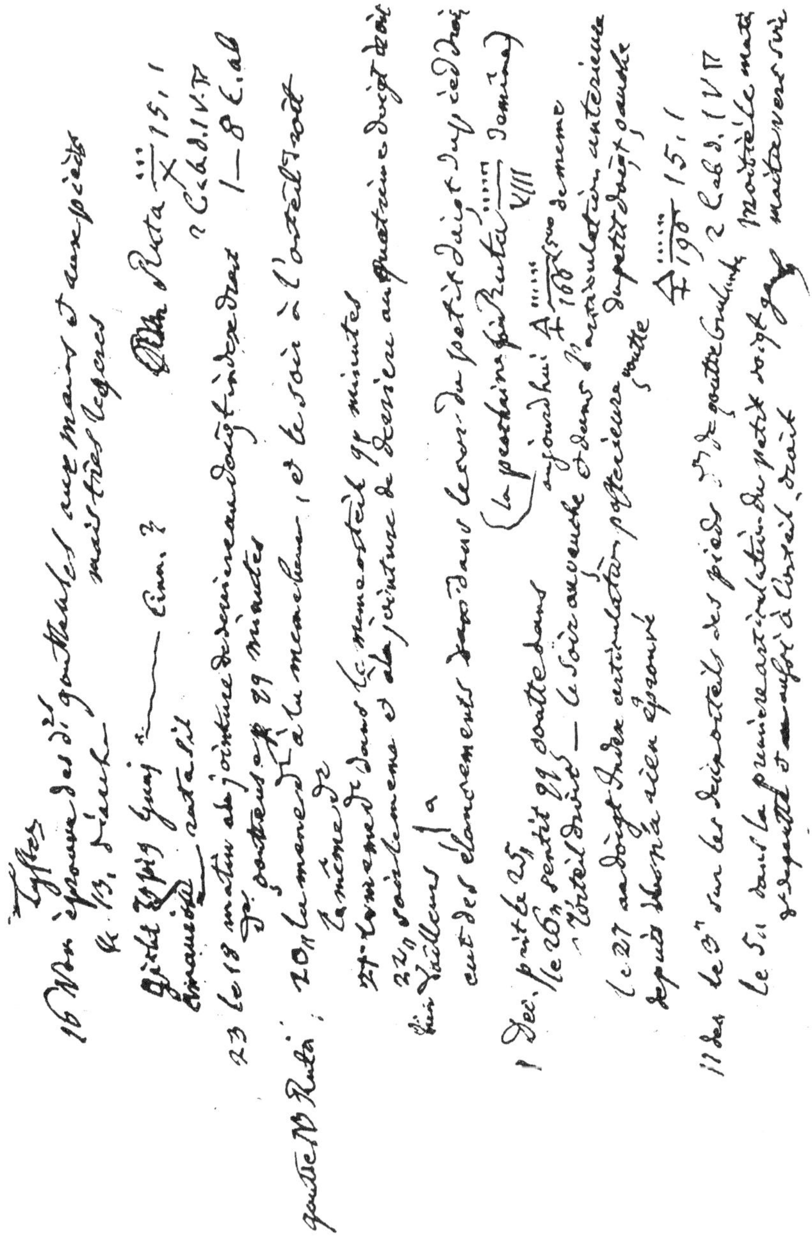

Mr Lyster: An extract from the case of Mr Robert Lyster, a man of letters suffering from gout and amaurosis. The entries refer to the period November 16th 1838 to January 6th 1839. Most of the entries on this page were made by Samuel but that for December 19th is in Melanie's hand. Note Hahnemann's experimentation with varying numbers of drops of the liquid remedy and his integration of two different scales of potency.

In his quest for the perfect dosage Hahnemann devised another method of taking the remedies for patients who were sufficiently careful to be accurate: 'I have lately found the following mode of administration preferable with careful patients. From a mixture of about five tablespoonfuls of pure water and five tablespoonfuls of French brandy, which is kept on hand in a bottle, 200, 300 or 400 drops (according as the solution is to be weaker or stronger) are dropped into a little vial, which may be half-filled with it, and in which the medicinal pellet or pellets of the medicine have been placed. This vial is stoppered and shaken until the medicine is dissolved. From this solution, one, two, three or several drops, according to the irritability [of nerve endings] and the vital force of the patient, are dropped into a cup, containing a spoonful of water; this is then well-stirred and given to the patient.'[23]

This method was used quite frequently in the early days and particularly during 1837 and 1838. Philippe Musard's first prescription was of this nature (see page 165). In April 1837 M. Auguste was given one drop of Sepia 24c (./VIII) diluted in 400 drops of a mixture [of water and brandy], of which 1 drop was to be put into 2 tablespoonfuls of water and from that a single small spoonful was to be drunk in the evenings. In October 1837 Baron Rothschild was instructed to pour 200 drops of a mixture (of water and brandy) onto a drop of Sulphur 24c (./VIII). He was to take 1–10 drops each morning. This technique was always reserved for a minority of patients and after 1838 Hahnemann rarely employed it, having found better ways to make accurate prescriptions for the sensitive. However, he continued to use it occasionally with some patients who were accustomed to the method and disposed to aggravations: the Reverend Everest and Philippe Musard (see Appendix I) were two such patients.

Another very occasional variant method of prescribing can be seen in the case of Amadée Burland, aged 20 months and still at the breast. His prescription, Hepar Sulph. 30c, ½ tablespoonful three times daily, was given to his wet nurse and the child was also to take a half-coffeespoonful of it in the mornings.

SUCCUSSION

It is clear from all this that by the time he settled in Paris, Hahnemann's invariable method of administering his remedies was that of frequent repetition of the remedy diluted in liquid: the method he had discussed in *Chronic Diseases*. His clearly expressed view by this time was that it was 'indispensable'[24] to take one and the same medicine repeatedly to secure the cure of a serious chronic disease. He had by then also developed a further refinement to minimise the possibility of aggravation from repeating exactly the same potency, suggesting that the liquid medicine, having been made up, should be slightly succussed between each dose because 'our vital principle cannot well bear that the same unchanged dose of medicine be given even twice in succession, much less more frequently . . . If the dose is in every case varied and modified a little in its degree of dynamisation, then the vital force of the patient will calmly, and as it were willingly, receive the same medicine even at brief intervals very many times in succession with the best results, every time increasing the well-being of the patient.'[25]

He advised that we 'potentise anew the medicinal solution (with perhaps eight, ten, twelve, succussions),'[26] but pointed out that the 'modification of the dynamisation is even effected if the bottle which contains the solution of one or more pellets is merely well shaken five or six times, every time before taking it.'[27]

The precise method of this intermediate succussion is not clearly indicated in the casebooks. There is normally no written instruction to shake the liquid between each repeated dose. This may mean that a standard procedure such as that outlined above was so common that it did not need to be written down. Only very occasionally is a succussion of the container of the liquid specified, usually in instances where a considerably greater number of succussions is advised. Usually, too, certainly in the early days, this appears to be a succussion of the stock bottle, or main container, rather than of an intermediate glass.

In May 1837 M. Auguste was instructed to put 1 teaspoonful of Platina 30c (. /X) in a vial with three tablespoonfuls [of liquid], to succuss 10 times and take one third morning, midday and night. This was after Platina 30c (. /X), prescribed without such succussion, had improved his condition considerably. In the last prescription he made for Mr Urchart, Hahnemann explicitly stated that the remedy was to be shaken 100 times.

When he prescribed a sequence of Cinnabar for Countess de Redarté, he instructed that each dose should be diluted in 4 tablespoonfuls and succussed: the first time 10 times, the second time 15 times. Mme Giffrier was instructed to succuss her dose of Sepia 24c (. /VIII) 200 times. However, it was the only prescription in her case where succussion is specified in this way. When he prescribed Cinnabar 30c (. /X) to Mme Bournichon in May 1838, he wrote that it was to be diluted in 15 tablespoonfuls. One teaspoonful was to be taken and then the liquid was to be succussed five or six times between each subsequent taking of a teaspoonful.

This technique appears to be the same as that used by some present-day homeopaths and referred to as 'plussing'. It should be noted, however, that Hahnemann himself does not use this term, and although for a brief period in 1840 he did use a notation involving the use of a plus sign in his prescriptions (see page 141), this notation does not appear to be attached to the above practice.

Subsequently he developed a further method of varying the dose, especially for sensitive patients. He suggested that after a dose had been diluted in a number of tablespoonfuls, one teaspoonful should be taken from the dilution and put into another glass, and then a teaspoonful be taken from that and so on, using perhaps a third or fourth glass:

'The solution of the medicinal globule of a thoroughly potentised medicine in a large quantity of water can be obviated (sic) by making a solution in only 7–8 tablespoonfuls of water and after thorough succussion of the vial take from it one tablespoonful and put it in a glass of water containing about 7–8 spoonfuls, this stirred thoroughly and then give a dose to the patient. If he is unusually excited and sensitive, a teaspoonful of this solution may be put in a second glass of water, thoroughly stirred and teaspoonful doses or more be given. There are patients of so great sensitiveness that a third or fourth glass similarly prepared may be necessary. Each such prepared glass must be made fresh daily, from which we give the patient one or (increasingly) several teaspoonful doses, in long lasting diseases daily or every second day, in acute diseases every two to six hours and in very urgent cases every hour or oftener. Thus in chronic diseases, every correctly chosen homeopathic medicine, even those whose action is of long duration, may be repeated daily for months with ever increasing success. If the solution is used up (in 7 to 15 days), it is necessary to add to the next solution of the same medicine if still indicated one or (though rarely) several pellets of a higher potency with which we continue so long as the patient experiences continued improvement without encountering one or another complaint that he never had before in his life . . . etc.'

From the description of this method of administration, as given in the *Organon*,[28] it has usually been considered that the method applied to the LM potency only, but it is clear from the casebooks that it was adopted by Hahnemann for use with the centesimal potencies, where needed. Already towards the end of 1837 we catch an occasional glimpse of his practice of instructing his patients to further dilute the remedies before taking them. In September 1837 M. Laburthe was instructed to dilute Hepar Sulph. 30c (. /X) in 30 tablespoonfuls of water and 3 of alcohol, to take one teaspoonful from the dilution and put it in a glass of water and then to take one teaspoonful from that each morning. Later the same month it was stated that he should continue with this prescription but should also shake the glass of water ten times and then put the contents into another glass, taking a teaspoonful from there mornings and evenings. In January 1838 M. Comeiras was prescribed Arsenicum 30c (. /X) in 15 tablespoonfuls in a glass of water: from that glass one tablespoonful was to be put into a second glass of water, from which a teaspoonful was to be taken and drunk. M. Comeiras was prescribed other remedies to be taken in this way.

In January 1838, Mme Michal was prescribed Arsenicum 30c (. /X) in fifteen [tablespoonfuls of water] and one [of alcohol]; one teaspoonful from this was to be put into a glass of water, this was to be shaken well. From it one teaspoonful was to be taken and added to a second glass of water. It was to be shaken as much again and one teaspoonful was to be taken out of it each morning. The glasses of water were to be thrown away each evening. When Mme Laplace responded to Sepia 30c (. /X) every four hours by producing fever at night, mucus from the rectum and pains in the left side of the uterus, Hahnemann instructed her to decant the remedies into a second glass. This system is used extensively in the cases of Mme Leloir, Mme and Mlle Guerouet and Mrs Boddington, for example.

OLFACTION

All these devices and methods appear to have been directed to reducing any aggravation which might have been caused by using remedies stronger than necessary. They were tried, modified and superseded as Hahnemann became more skilful in attenuating his doses. One of the chief means he had of rendering his doses more refined was that of olfaction: the patient was asked to inhale the remedy which had been diluted in liquid. This was a method he had first introduced in 1829 and never subsequently abandoned.[29] He used it throughout the period of the Paris practice, and used it quite regularly with several patients, for instance, Miss Dunsford, Mlle Denis, Mme Morrisse and the Reverend Everest. Normally Hahnemann asked his patient to inhale the remedy there and then in the consulting room, and usually gave them another remedy, often sac lac, to take daily at home thereafter. Occasionally we read of patients inhaling remedies on their own initiative at home. With some patients the practice was sparingly employed, with others more regularly. Many of the latter were those whom Hahnemann had grown to regard as sensitive to remedies. Even within the method of olfaction he created grades to suit each person: sometimes he instructed the patient to inhale strongly, sometimes just a little. He occasionally noted that too strong an inhalation had caused an aggravation.

To sum up: at this stage in his practice, Hahnemann seems to have been advising that remedies prepared according to the rules for the centesimal potency should be administered in the following way:

1) Take one (or more) drops of the remedy potentised to the desired degree.
2) Add the medicine to 7 (or 8, 15, 20, 30, 40) (table)spoonfuls of water and alcohol, or water and charcoal in a vial.
3) Take from this glass or vial one small coffee- or teaspoonful of liquid as often as indicated.
4) Succuss the vial as indicated between each repetition of the dose.
5) For patients for whom this method causes an aggravation of symptoms, after having put a small spoonful in a glass and succussed it, take a small spoonful out of that glass and put it into a second with water and alcohol. Take a small spoonful from the second glass. The process may be repeated in a third or even a fourth glass.
6) Repeat the dose as often as indicated.
7) For those patients who are still subject to aggravations by this method, use olfaction.

DESCENDING POTENCIES

It will be apparent from the examples already cited that Hahnemann used the range of the centesimal potencies in a rather different way from modern homeopaths. In the first place he used different points on the scale from those commonly used today – 30, 24, 18, 12, 6, 3 – and in the second he invariably started treatment with the highest potency he intended to use, and gradually descended the scale (in the first years of his Paris practice).

For instance, Count Schowaloff came in 1836 complaining of having had severe migraines for ten years, several times a week. He received four prescriptions over a period of a month: first, Sulphur 24c (. /VIII) one drop diluted in 15 tablespoonfuls of liquid, [one spoonful to be taken each day]. After this his headache completely disappeared, so Sulphur was continued in the same potency but less dilute: Sulphur 24c (. . /VIII), two drops diluted in 7 tablespoonfuls of water and alcohol. After this the count had another migraine, but only one over a fortnight and that after drinking too much wine and champagne. Then the potency was changed: he was given three drops of Sulphur 18c (. . . /VI), dissolved in 15 tablespoonfuls [of liquid]. The following week he was given 4 drops of Sulphur 12c (. . . . /IV) in 15 tablespoon-fuls, one spoonful to be taken each evening, and he was subsequently pronounced completely cured.

For the first three years of the Paris practice this was the only method and scale of potency Hahnemann used. The following years, however, were to see an enormous amount of experimentation with potencies.

NOTES

1. Hahnemann wrote in *Chronic Diseases* in 1834 (though the book was not published until 1838) that he had begun to prescribe in liquid doses. There are scarcely any references to dry doses in the casebooks – an exception is Mrs Boddington, who was given Opium 30c in dry doses to take as she felt the need.
2. See Hans Henne, *Hahnemanns Krankenjournale* Nos. 2 & 3, Stuttgart 1963.
3. S. Hahnemann, 'Cure and Prevention of Scarlet Fever', *Lesser Writings*, ed. R. E. Dudgeon, p. 432.
4. Printed and translated in *Lesser Writings*, ed. R. E. Dudgeon, pp. 443ff.
5. See Henne, *op. cit.*, and the early casebooks.
6. C. Wheeler, *Organon of the Rational Art of Healing*, 1st edn, paragraph 247.
7. Comments about the amount of succussion required are to be found throughout Hahnemann's writings, from the earliest in the 2nd edition of the *Organon*, where he wrote of Drosera that 'each dilution having had 20 shakes will be dangerously potent to a whooping cough patient, whereas the same dilution with only 2 shakes will be curative and safe.' See also *Organon*, 5th edn, trans. R. E. Dudgeon, p. 270, note, where Hahnemann writes that he has now fixed on '2 successions for each vial, in preference to the greater number formerly employed.'

He changed his practice yet again in later years and wrote in *Chronic Diseases*: 'During the last years, since I have been giving every dose of medicine in a solution, divided over 15, 20 or 30 days and even more, no potentising in an attenuating vial is found too strong, and again I use ten strokes.' Preface to *Die chronischen Krankheiten*, Vol. 3, written 1834, published 1838. See Tafel's English translation of *Chronic Diseases*, pp. 268–9).

8. Hahnemann, *Materia Medica Pura*, Vol. 6.

9. See H. L. Coulter, *Homeopathic Medicine and Modern Science*, 2nd ed., for a bibliography of this topic up till 1980, and see further Peter Fisher, 'Research in Homeopathy: A Selected, Annotated Bibliography', *Journal of the American Institute of Homeopathy*, March 1987, Vol. 80, No. 1, pp. 26–31.

10. Haehl, *op. cit.*, Vol. 1, p. 323.

11. See Hahnemann, *Organon*, 1st (1810) edn, trans. C. Wheeler, paragraph 201.

12. See Hahnemann, *Organon*, 5th edn, trans. R. E. Dudgeon, paragraph 246.

13. See Hahnemann, *Organon*, 5th edn, trans. R. E. Dudgeon, paragraph 246 note.

14. = 30c.

15. See Hahnemann, *Organon*, 5th edn, trans. R. E. Dudgeon, paragraph 246 note.

16. S. Hahnemann, Preface to Vol. 3 of *Die chronischen Krankheiten*, trans. Tafel as *Chronic Diseases*, p. 262.

17. *ibid.*, p. 263.

18. *ibid.*, pp. 254–5. See Revd Everest, letter published in *The Homoeopathic Times*, Vol. 4, p. 731.

19. Hahnemann clearly considered the amount of the dose to be important for a long period of time. Even towards the end of his life he still occasionally varied the number of drops or pellets given at one time. In 1841 he prescribed Euphorbium several times for a M. Framin and used the following sequence of doses and potencies: . /X, . /VIII, . . /VI, . . /IV and . . . /II.

20. Hans Ritter, *Samuel Hahnemann*, Heidelberg 1974, p. 122, described Hahnemann's notation as being like the Seventh Seal of the Apocalypse, but in fact most of Hahnemann's signs and symbols were those in common use in his day and may be found in G. Weber, *Codex des médicaments homoéopathiques*, Paris 1854. Henne has also explained most of them in the work cited in Note 2 above. The abbreviations are very like those used by Dr Sebastien Des Guidi and

these are clearly explained by Dr Jacques Baur in his study of Des Guidi, *Les manuscrits du Docteur Comte Sebastien Des Guidi*, Lyon 1985 and 1986. It is not the technical abbreviations which present a problem in Hahnemann's casebooks but his personal ones, where the expansion is often uncertain.

21. John Tomlinson, 'Doses, Dilution and the LM Potencies', *The Homoeopath*, December 1990, Vol. 10, No. 4, pp. 100–106. Also see P. Barthel, 'Hahnemann's Legacy – the Q (LM) Potencies' in *British Homoeopathic Journal*, April 1991, Vol. 80, pp. 112–21.
22. S. Hahnemann, *Die chronischen Krankheiten*, trans. Tafel p. 266.
23. *ibid.*, p. 267. 24. *ibid.*, p. 263. 25. *ibid.*, p. 263.
26. S. Hahnemann, *Organon*, 6th edn, paragraph 248.
27. S. Hahnemann, *Chronic Diseases*, Preface to Vol. 3, p. 264.
28. S. Hahnemann, *Organon*, 6th edn, paragraph 248 note.
29. Haehl, *op. cit.*, Vol. 1, pp. 181–2 writes that Hahnemann abandoned the process of olfaction 'especially in his Paris period'. Haehl noted that Hahnemann was still writing about the process approvingly in 1837 (Haehl, 1, 324) but assumed that Hahnemann's striking all detailed reference to it from the 6th edition of the *Organon* meant that Hahnemann had abandoned its use. However, from looking at the actual cases it is clear that Hahnemann had not stopped using it at all. Indeed, in some later cases the patient seems to take almost all the active remedies by olfaction. Take the case of Mlle Denis for instance. She first came for treatment in July 1841 and though her first two remedies were administered conventionally in water, Hahnemann thereafter started to use olfaction and repeatedly asked her to inhale Carbo Animalis in the consulting room while giving her sac lac to take daily at home. Later in the same case she was asked to inhale Kali Carbonicum, Natrum Phosphoricum and China.

Hahnemann may have thought olfaction was a much more effective way of giving the remedy in general and not just a means of avoiding aggravation, for whenever he used the technique he gave the patient only a single dose. Usually the patient was also given a daily prescription of another remedy to take home. Normally this was sac lac but sometimes, especially in the early years, another active remedy. So, when he gave Mme Braun Cicuta Virosa, he gave her Cicuta Virosa . . . . . . /X to inhale and at the same time gave her sac lac for eight days to take at home. M. Musard clearly inhales Opium on page 179. As in all attempts to clarify Hahnemann's abbreviations, the question is not always as clear as in these instances.

Chapter 9

The Ultimate Attenuation

Hahnemann continued to administer his remedies in the way outlined in the previous chapter until mid-1838. Around this time, however, he began to use a higher range of the centesimal potencies in addition to the range he had been using hitherto: he now began to use centesimal potencies up to 200.

By 1838, of course, others had begun to investigate the fascinating topic of the potentisation of remedies. Two great experimenters, Korsakoff and Jenichen, had been building on Hahnemann's findings relating to the power of the dose increasing in proportion to the amount of succussion and dilution to which the remedy was subjected. By various methods they had individually succeeded in producing potencies attenuated to 1000c and 1500c (even higher later).[1] This was way beyond the lower potencies with which Hahnemann had been content for so long. However, although he had apparently tried these very high potencies, he was uneasy with them, probably because he had not made them himself and was not therefore quite sure how they had been prepared.[2] When he began to use higher potencies on a regular basis he therefore restricted himself to those lower than 200c, which he was able to prepare himself, by hand. He used these increasingly often during his time in Paris.

One of the earliest examples of Hahnemann's use of these higher potencies occurs in the case of M. Barré, who first visited the practice in 1837, suffering from epilepsy. During the first year of his treatment he had been prescribed a number of different remedies, initially Valerian 30c (. /X) and Cuprum 30c (. /X) in the acute stages of the illness and then a number of remedies including Sulphur, Cuprum, Calcarea Carbonica, Hepar Sulph., Pulsatilla, Magnesia Carbonica, Belladonna, Kali Carbonicum, Arsenicum and Aethusa, in potencies ranging from 30c (. /X) in a descending scale to 6c (. /II). By September 1838 he had been taking Sulphur 30c (. /X) daily followed by sac lac daily for over a month. His condition had improved considerably over the year of treatment but seemed to have reached a plateau. On September 29th, 1838, Hahnemann prescribed one of the high potency remedies for him for the first time, giving him Sulphur 100c (. /C) daily for over a week and following this with Sulphur 95c (. /95) daily for over a week and then Sulphur 90c (. /90) daily for a further week, before suddenly switching to Sulphur 185c (. /185) daily and going on to 199c (. /199) at the following appointment, and then 200c (. /200) after that. When he was prescribed the 200c, M. Barré was also instructed to shake the glass 200 times as well and take a teaspoonful out of it.

With these higher potencies, M. Barré's condition began to improve once more and he was able to discontinue treatment shortly afterwards, in February 1839. He had no further need to consult the Hahnemanns until a year later, in 1840, when he returned about another problem and reported that he had had no further epileptic attacks.

M. Collmann began treatment for a skin eruption of eight years standing on September 3rd, 1838. The first prescription was Sulphur 30c (. /X), one teaspoonful to be taken daily from a mixture of remedies, water and alcohol in a glass. There was no improvement and so, on his return, Hahnemann prescribed Sulphur 100c (. /C), one teaspoonful each morning. M. Collmann's skin then improved and Hahnemann continued to prescribe Sulphur on this new scale, in descending potencies: 95c was the next prescription, followed by 90c and then 85c. On November 21st, while M. Collmann was still improving, Hahnemann suddenly began to use ascending potencies; starting with Sulphur 158c, he climbed up through 159c, 160c, 165c, 167c till May 27th, 1839, when, after a tremendous improvement in his patient, he rejected the mild increase to 168c which he had intended and had already written in his book, crossed that out and leapt to 181c. M. Collmann continued to improve.

EXPERIMENTING WITH THE SCALE

In general these new higher potencies were, when first introduced, used in a descending scale, as the lower potencies had been. Soon, however, Hahnemann took to using them in an ascending scale and this became the norm. Quite commonly, in the early stages of the use of this range of potencies, we find him using both ascending and descending scales in the same case, as in the two cases cited above. In cases begun later, however, it was normal for him to prescribe on an ascending scale throughout.

There are various gradations used on the scale and it is not always clear to me what it was hoped to achieve by the use of the different potencies. Sometimes the scale descended or ascended in fives, sometimes in ones, sometimes in a less regular gradation. There is a tendency to bunching of the potencies in prescribing; that is Hahnemann would begin prescribing with, say, 168c and subsequent prescribing would tend to cluster round 168c. If he began with 191c, then the prescribing would cluster round that. There seems to be no way of recovering the reasons why he should have started with one of these potencies rather than another.

As with the lower potencies, Hahnemann normally diluted only one drop in the liquid in the vial, but on occasion used more than one. To Mme Leffroy, for instance, who suffered from severe headaches and had had a lot of bleeding and constipation, he prescribed five drops of Sulphur 90c (. . . . . /90).

These potencies were dispensed in the same way as the lower potencies: repeatedly in a dilution of water and alcohol. Although there was still no regular mention of succussion between repetition of doses, the same method seems to have been adopted as with the lower potencies and a number is occasionally specified, as in the case of M. Barré above. In the case of Mme Leffroy, too, we may note that her last prescription was the same potency as the penultimate one, but that it was to be 'succussed 100 times'.

Once Hahnemann had begun to use potencies in this way, he seems to have tended to use the higher potencies for the remedy he saw as directed at the chronic or miasmatic treatment, and the lower for the remedy he saw as directed at acute or transient symptoms. Characteristically, he prescribed Sulphur in the higher potencies and other remedies in the lower. So, for example, in October 1838 Mme Laplace consulted the Hahnemanns, complaining of difficulty with her periods, pain and vomiting up to twenty-five times a day. Hahnemann prescribed Sulphur for several weeks in a sequence 100c to 86c (. /C, . /95, . /90, . /86) and the periods improved. However, at this point the patient developed a fever accompanied by pains in the joints and Hahnemann prescribed Aconite 30c (. /X) from the other scale, following this with Nux Vomica 30c (. /X) in response to a constipated state which ensued. When Mme Laplace was fully recovered from her acute illness, Hahnemann reverted to the use of Sulphur, this time in an even higher potency than he had been using before, 158c (. /158).

He also continued to experiment with the dilutions and increasingly used more than one glass to dispense the remedy. For instance, in 1838

Prince Mettshersky was prescribed Mercurius Solubilis 24c (. /24), one tablespoonful to be put into a glass, from which one small spoonful was to be taken and put into a second glass. It is noteworthy that Hahnemann was inclined to follow this practice where he suspected there might be aggravation. In 1839, when Sheila Brugmann's first prescription of Sulphur 180c diluted in one glass caused an aggravation, he subsequently instructed that the remedy be decanted into a second glass.

Throughout 1840 his experimentation with potencies increased. In the spring of 1840 he began to write, for example, . /193/100 instead of simply . /193, apparently to indicate the potency 193c. Around this period this expression is found repeatedly. For Gabriel de Massarelles we see the following notation in successive prescriptions of Sulphur from February 1840: . /190/100; . /190/100; . 192/100; . 193/100; . 195/100. (See also the case of M. Musard in Appendix I.) I am not sure precisely what is the purpose of this notation. It is possible that Hahnemann was already beginning to experiment with greater dilutions than the 1:100 of the centesimal scale and that his use of this denominator was a confirmation to himself that he was in fact using the centesimal scale.

Shortly after this time he began commonly to prescribe remedies in a potency indicated by numbers again at the lower end of the scale, but now used arabic numerals rather than Roman. We find notations such as . /24, . /48 used regularly. A little later such notations are found with a plus after them: 25+ ; 30+ ; 48+ etc., and even later, with sometimes a double plus: 24++, 48++ etc.

In the case of Gabriel de Massarelles, after the long series of prescriptions of Sulphur . /190/100; . /192/100; . /193/100; . /195/100 mentioned above, Hahnemann suddenly began to prescribe Sulphur 17+; 18+; 19+; 20+; 21+; 22+; 23+; 24+; 25+, then 24+; 23+; 22+; 21+; 20++.

The significance of these subtle distinctions is unclear to me. However, it seems likely that the notation represents some intermediate stage on the way to the use of the LM scale, which is discussed in the following pages. It does not seem to refer to the method of succussion known as plussing.

THE LM POTENCY

Hahnemann had apparently gone as far as he wanted to with the centesimal potencies by this time. The now routine dilution of the remedies into one, two or three glasses and his frequent use of olfaction show that one of his main concerns in prescribing was to give as diluted a dose as possible. In fact, in his published work, he frequently wrote of dilutions and attenuations rather than of dynamisations or potentisations. In the 1840s he was looking for a way to attenuate his remedies even more.

There was a good deal of contemporary controversy about the use or uselessness of the higher centesimal potencies already developed. Some homeopaths, while observing the principle of similars, were still reluctant to use potencies even as high as 30c, being unable to accept that they worked. Hahnemann had no such doubts in principle, but he was dubious about the current methods of preparing the higher centesimal potencies.

His chief objection to the use of very highly potentised remedies in the centesimal potency was that he thought they might cause too great an aggravation of the patient's symptoms. The ratio of substance to diluent (1:100) was, he thought, so small that very powerful succussion would be needed to raise the remedy to a much higher level of dynamisation. He feared that such a succussion would have to be mechanical and therefore too violent and more likely to cause aggravations.[3]

He therefore set about developing a new system of dilution and succussion which would enable him to produce very highly attenuated remedies without the violent succussion and the accompanying danger of aggravation of symptoms. Eventually he evolved a method and produced a new scale of potency which he called the LM potency. He regarded this as altogether gentler in its approach than the centesimal potencies, largely because it was subject to far more dilution: 1: 50,000 rather than 1:100. He also seems to have regarded remedies prepared on the LM scale as being more highly potentised or dynamised than those prepared on the centesimal scale.[4]

He seems to have begun to use the LM potency in his practice towards the end of 1840. His first use of it appears to have been while treating the musician M. Rousselot, who had been ill for three years, suffering from severe attacks of 'vertigo' during which he could not speak, could see only stars, could hear voices speaking but could not understand them. He was also beginning to go deaf. M. Rousselot had first consulted the Hahnemanns in October 1837 and had been treated with a range of remedies in the centesimal potency. On December 16th 1840 he was given one globule of Sulphur LM 10 (. /10/o) dispensed from one glass of water, thus becoming the first person to receive the new LM potency. The notation with 'o' indicates Hahnemann's use now of globules instead of drops. The use of globules is normally taken to indicate the use of what we now call the LM potency, prepared with globules.

Having devised this new potency, Hahnemann proceeded to use it increasingly frequently in his practice. He administered and prescribed it in the way he had become used to prescribing his centesimal potencies, that is, diluted in liquid from which doses of 1, 2, 3, 4 or more spoonfuls were taken as required. In the cases of especially sensitive patients, the recent modification of decanting into a second or third glass was employed and in fact, as he developed the use of the LM potency, this appears to have become the standard method of prescription. However, he did not see this as a method peculiar to the LM potency, but simply as a continuation of the method he had been using with the centesimal potency for some time.

Despite his triumphant invention of this attenuation, Hahnemann himself did not use very many remedies in the LM potency. I have only noted in these casebooks his use of Sulphur, Calcarea Carbonica, Graphites, Silica, Lycopodium, Natrum Muriaticum, Nux Vomica, Phosphorus, Hepar Sulph., Belladonna, Bryonia and Opium.[5] On the whole he seems to have preserved his use of it for those remedies which he repeated frequently. Most of his prescribing in the new potency was therefore of Sulphur.

When Hahnemann described the use of the LM potency in the *Organon*, he seemed to suggest that it should always be prescribed in an ascending scale and that there should be no leaps in the scale.[6] In fact we can see from the casebooks that he did sometimes use at least Sulphur LM in a descending scale, and did sometimes allow leaps. For instance, the sculptor M. Richome was prescribed a sequence of Sulphur LM 11, 10, 15, 10, 15, 16, 7, 8, 9. On the whole, however, Hahnemann used the LM potencies in an ascending scale with no leaps, and he always prescribed remedies other than Sulphur in this way when he prescribed them in the LM potency. He did not, however, always start with the lowest LM potency. For remedies other than Sulphur he hardly ever used a potency higher than LM 7. LM 24 is the highest potency I can discover in Sulphur and it was rare for him to go above 20.[7] Once again we see that Hahnemann was prepared to experiment.

At first he used the LM potencies in a way comparable to that in which he had previously used the higher centesimal potencies. He used the fundamental chronic remedy, usually Sulphur, in the LM potency and continued to use the lower centesimal potencies for the acute and transient symptoms. He used either a high centesimal potency or the LM potency at any time when he was liable to be repeating a remedy for some while.

Mlle de Baunaud, for instance, was treated from May 11th 1841, for severe headaches and congestion of blood to the head with redness of the face. She also suffered from vertigo. Hahnemann began his prescribing with the standard one teaspoonful of Sulphur LM 4 daily, taken from a dilution of one tablespoonful of the remedy into one glass of water, then followed up with sac lac daily for the next two prescriptions, then Sulphur LM 7, then sac lac. His patient then presented with throat and ear pain and was given Chamomilla 30c, one teaspoonful daily from a dilution of one tablespoonful in one glass of liquid. The condition improved but she returned on November 17th with a sore throat for which she was given Phosphorus 30c (one teaspoonful daily from a dilution of seven tablespoonfuls in a glass of liquid) for a week. This was subsequently continued for a further week. When her acute state had improved, Hahnemann reverted to the use of Sulphur, this time in an LM 8, until she was completely better.

He did not always use the LM potency, even when he had it. Even as late as April 1842 he treated M. Tarbocher with Nux Vomica 199c and a whole series of remedies in the centesimal potency, without using any LM potencies at all. He also asked M. Tarbocher to inhale many of his remedies, possibly as an alternative to using the LM potency. Mlle Denis was treated during the LM period (July 1840 and later), but was instructed to inhale most of her remedies in centesimal potencies, with the exception of a few acute remedies which were administered orally in a low centesimal potency. Mme Morrisse and the Reverend Everest were also notable inhalers, apparently of centesimal potencies, during the LM period. In Mme Framin's case Hahnemann moved straight into prescribing LMs of Sulphur and Hepar Sulph., concurrently with numerous remedies to be inhaled in both centesimal and LM potencies. Occasionally he even preferred to use Sulphur in a centesimal potency: in a very late case he prescribed Nux Vomica LM 1 to Mme Lemoine and followed this up with Sulphur 30c (. . . . . . /X), a reversion to a very old-fashioned use of several drops in the dose.

It is notable that Hahnemann rarely asked his patients to inhale the LM potencies. Presumably he thought that these potencies were themselves quite sufficiently diluted and attenuated without needing to be inhaled. Exceptions are found of course, especially in the case of Mme Morrisse.

As time went on, Hahnemann was more inclined to use Sulphur in the LM potency to the exclusion of other remedies, ignoring the emergence of acutes more often than he had done previously. In the case of Mme Champagny, who first came to see him in May 1841, he began the treatment with Sulphur LM 4 and continued to repeat the Sulphur in ever higher degrees of the LM potency up to 9, interspersed with sac lac. By June 1841 she was much improved and stopped coming.

As already mentioned, the new potency was called the LM potency (50,000 = LM in Roman numerals) because, roughly speaking, the ratio of substance to diluent was 1:50,000 (compared with the 1:100 ratio of the centesimal potency). In the final edition of his *Organon* Hahnemann explained that it was to be made by the following process:

a) Take a grain of a 3c remedy (because all remedies are soluble in water at this point).
b) Dissolve this grain in 500 drops of a mixture of water and wine (one part brandywine and four parts distilled water).
c) Take a single drop from this liquid (a drop such as could be absorbed only by 500 globules) and put it in a vial.
d) Add to this drop 100 drops of alcohol (rectified wine spirit).
e) Succuss the liquid 100 times by hand against a hard but elastic object. (This produces the first degree of dynamisation, the ratio between the medicine and the diluent being 1:50,000.)
f) Moisten sugar globules with the liquid and allow them to dry.[8]

The globules are of such a size that 500 of them can hardly take up one drop of liquid. This ensures that at subsequent stages of potentisation the ratio of medicine to diluent remains at 1:50,000 or higher – at this stage one medicated globule is dissolved in one drop of water in a second vial and dynamised with 100 drops of 95° grain alcohol by means of 100 successions. Globules are moistened as before and the process can be continued as far as required.

As Hahnemann describes the process in the *Organon*, and as he talks of its implications, his excitement is transmitted to the reader. He had finally released spirit from matter, or energy from mass, as we would now say, achieved the transmutation which had been the goal of alchemists and chemists for thousands of years: 'The medicinal substance that seems to us in its crude state to be only matter, sometimes even non-medicinal matter, is at last completely transformed and refined by these progressive dynamisations to become a spirit-like medicinal force. This spirit-like medicinal force by itself is no longer perceptible to the senses, but the medicated globule acts as its carrier and demonstrates its curative power in the sick organism.'[9]

It is clear from the casebooks that the LM potency emerged from Hahnemann's practice merely as the logical extension of his quest for the perfectly attenuated medicine, the medicine which would act as gently, as permanently, as quickly and as harmlessly as possible to cure the patient.

NOTES

1. See G. Weber, *Les hautes puissances*, Paris 1847, p. 79.

2. Although it is said that he used such higher potencies, there are no examples of this in the Paris casebooks.

3. *Organon*, 6th edn, paragraph 270, note f. He also disapproved of the no-dilution method of preparation.

4. *Organon*, 6th edn, paragraph 270.

5. Other remedies survive in the LM potency in Hahnemann's remedy boxes. See the list of their contents given in Haehl, *op. cit.*

6. *Organon*, 6th edn, paragraphs 280-281 and see Tomlinson, *art. cit.* and Barthel, *art. cit.*

7. Barthel appears to be mistaken when he describes Hahnemann's use of the LM potencies, stating that Hahnemann's case records give clear evidence that treatment would start with the 1Q (1 LM), *(art. cit.,* p. 116).

8. *Organon*, 6th edn, paragraph 270 ff.

9. *Organon*, 6th edn, paragraph 270.

Appendix I

Further Cases

Name: BRAUN, Mme
Age 48, married, 4 children

Casebook entries: **2**/16, 17

This short and relatively successful case shows Hahnemann's early Paris methods.

In Mme Braun's case there were three stages. In the first, lasting from December 1835 to July 1836, her main problems were insomnia, inflammation and pain in the eyes, and a craving for charcoal. The insomnia disappeared after the first prescription (Sulphur 30c) but the other conditions remained. Hahnemann continued with the Sulphur 30c for a while and then introduced sac lac, and after this the eye pain went. She felt better but developed a general sort of vague malaise.

At this juncture Hahnemann gave his patient Merc. Sol. 30c to inhale, followed by liquid doses of sac lac and Hepar Sulph. 30c for three weeks. She was much improved after this, but now complained of sharp pains in her wrists and feet and reported that the craving for charcoal was stronger than ever. Prescribing apparently on this strange, rare and peculiar symptom Hahnemann gave her Cicuta Virosa to inhale, and although the craving only disappeared for a day, the pains in her wrists and feet also seemed to clear up. He then prescribed Cinnabar and sac lac to follow, and on her next visit some three weeks later she was much better and the craving for charcoal was much less: he continued the sac lac. However, she returned eight days later, complaining of bruising pains (old symptoms), the return of the charcoal craving and the beginning of the return of the eye problem.

Hahnemann then prescribed Carbo Veg. 30c, perhaps still guided by the craving for charcoal. This remedy did not affect the desire for charcoal but did bring back the pain in the eyes for five days, until she stopped taking it, and at the same time her joints became progressively more painful – 'flying gout' – Hahnemann called the condition. He then prescribed Calc. Carb. 30c but this had no discernible effect on any symptoms. Eventually the joints seemed to become gradually less painful as the eye inflammation re-established itself. Hahnemann then prescribed Silica 30c after repertorising 'tearing pains in the eyes', and was at last rewarded by a general improvement which was especially marked in her emotional disposition – she was no longer melancholy or cantankerous. Her improvement continued and after further prescriptions of Silica 24c and 18c she did not need treatment for a long time.

The second phase of treatment began in April of the following year, 1837, when Mme Braun came back because the eye pains had returned very violently. After repertorising, Hahnemann prescribed Ant. Crud. 30c, but this seemed to do little and so Nux Vomica was prescribed (which had not appeared in the repertorisation for the eye symptoms but was given on the basis of hot flushes). This remedy seemed to clear up the eye symptoms but not the hot flushes! However, Hahnemann continued to prescribe it, going down to the 24c potency, and at that point the hot flushes improved a lot while the patient remained free from eye pain. After this, Hahnemann went back to prescribing Hepar Sulph., which he had first prescribed near the outset of treatment. After prescriptions of Hepar Sulph. 24c, 18c and 12c, Mme Braun was reported to be perfectly well and remained so for a year.

The third phase of treatment began when she returned in July 1838 because her symptoms had all come back – a little. Once again her eyes had been giving trouble, and she now also had a troublesome vaginal discharge having had some menstrual bleeding after five years free of this. Hahnemann prescribed Sulphur 30c and 24c and then Hepar Sulph. 24c, and we hear no more of Mme Braun. Does this mean that she was cured permanently or that she abandoned homeopathy?

All the prescribing in this early Paris case is in potencies of 30c and lower, prescribed in liquid. Mme Braun was clearly a robust patient and there was no need to protect her from aggravations by using olfaction or extensive dilution of remedies. It is notable that on one occasion, when Hahnemann did prescribe an inhaled remedy for her, Mme Braun had a rapid improvement followed by a severe aggravation (Cicuta, February 14th 1836).

Overall the case demonstrates Hahnemann's propensity at this stage of his practice to use sac lac while watching and waiting, and to prescribe for all symptoms as they emerged in the middle of chronic treatment, whether they were acutes, old symptoms or new symptoms.

Casebook entry:**2**/17

December 9th [1835]
When pregnant with her first child she suffered terrible vomiting for which she was given various treatments including an infusion of absinthe which made her salivate so much that she had soaked twelve or fifteen towels in twelve days. Three months into the pregnancy she started to have a craving to eat charcoal: this craving ceased for three years. When she became pregnant again the craving for charcoal returned even more strongly and ceased with the confinement. She had the same craving with her third child and it has never left her since.
Now, she has had no periods for twenty months: whenever she is without periods or is pregnant the desire to eat charcoal is much stronger. She cannot prevent herself from eating it. She only chews it, but does not crave it any less.
Seven years ago she started to get pain in her eyes for no reason, tearing pains inside the eye, no headache.
She has been without periods for twenty months.
She drinks coffee, which she will stop.
Thirsty.
She has been bled 11 times this year.

Repertory
(G) Tearing pains in the eyes: Asar., Kal., Led., Lyc., Nux Vom., Puls., Squill., Verat., Zincum, Bell., Lyc.
Alum., Anac., Calc., Mez., Magn., Nat. Phos., Sep.

Prescription
Sulphur 30c (. /X) diluted in 15 tablespoonfuls.

December 19th [1835]
The pains in the eyes have continued, burning pains. In the other eye there is great heat (*without redness*).
She does not take coffee any more; she is not constipated.
She is thirsty especially at night.
She has no leucorrhoea; she is sleeping calmly, which she has not done for eighteen years.

Prescription
Sulphur 30c (. /X) to be added to the previous medication and then continue with sac lac diluted in 15 [tablespoonfuls].

January 14th [1836]
The pain and inflammation in her eyes has gone.
She is thirsty at night; she sleeps well; she has a little diarrhoea.
She has developed a peculiar taste for maize flour which she eats raw.

Prescription
Today sac lac diluted in 7 tablespoonfuls.
(Cicuta for the taste for charcoal.)

January 23rd [1836]
She has no further pain in her eyes; in the evening her head feels hot
but it cools down later. She can see better, with more confidence.
She is thirsty at night.
She has a generalised feeling of not being well, as if she had a fever.

Prescription
Inhale Merc. Sol. 30c (. /X). Then:
No. 1. Dilute sac lac in 7 tablespoonfuls.
No. 2. Dilute Hepar Sulph. 30c (. . /X) in 15 tablespoonfuls.

February 14th [1836]
(49 years old. Hasn't had periods for 2 years)
She's feeling very well, sleeping well. Everything's going well.
She has sharp pains in her wrists and in the joints in her feet, night and
morning. She can't shake hands.
She has ringing and pounding in her ears when her eye is about to give
problems.
She has had no pain in the eyes since the 25th December. Sometimes,
but rarely, she has had twinges in her eyes especially in the right eye,
intermittent pains which last eight or ten minutes instead of eight or ten
days.
The craving for charcoal is more violent than ever.

Prescription
Cicuta 30c (. . . . . . /X) to inhale and then sac lac for eight days.

February 25th [1836]
She has been sniffling more than usual. The whites of her eyes are
a little bloodshot but without pain: this has never happened before.
Inflammation always accompanied pain before.

The throbbing in the ears which previously always preceded great inflammation came for a moment but passed.

She has an enormous desire to eat charcoal. This craving disappeared entirely for a day.

Yesterday evening she had a very bad headache and nausea.

The pains in her wrists and feet have passed.

She has had hot flushes with sweats once or twice a day for a year.

Her stools have normally been dark and she has had diarrhoea only once.

Prescription
No 1. Cinnabar 30c (. . . /X) in 15 [table]spoonfuls.
No. 2. Sac lac in 7 [table]spoonfuls.

March 17th [1836]

Her eyes are perfect. She has had a little swelling of the gums which lessens in the daytime. She still likes charcoal. She's sleeping well. At night much troubled with rising heat.

She is sniffling a lot – she has had a cold.

She eats much less charcoal, she has less desire for it.

She has more energy.

Her eyes are much stronger, she can see the Registers.

Prescription
Sac lac in 7 tablespoonfuls.

March 26th [1836]

Some eight days ago she had a strong bruising pain in her left shoulder, (old symptom) even while resting.

Dull bruising pains in her knees on bending.

Two days ago she had a little redness in the inside of the eye which spread to cover the whole of the white of the eye; there was a momentary throbbing in her eye.

The excessive desire to eat charcoal has returned in force. She notices that the craving is more severe than when she was more ill.

She had a kind of diarrhoea for four months and since that time has had 15 good stools; it is also since then that the craving for charcoal has returned, this is especially strong towards noon.

Prescription
Carbo Veg. 30c (. /X) in 7 [table]spoonfuls.

April 9th [1836]
She has bruised pains in her swollen knee. She had this condition last year.
She had pain in her eyes for 5 days and then she stopped taking the Carbo Veg. Then her left hand began to itch a lot and her thumb swelled up like a sausage and her hand was very red, then the eye became less red, now it is alright.
She had the same pain in her wrist as in her knee but that has passed.
Everyday she has the same desire for charcoal but she has abstained from eating it.
These pains seem to be 'flying gout'.
She says that all these symptoms are ones that she has already suffered but they are much less.
(Carbo Veg./Cinn./Cic. inhaled/Hepar Sulph./Merc. Sol. inhaled. Sulphur/Sulphur)

Prescription
Calc. Carb. 30c (. /X) in 15 [table]spoonfuls.

May 14th [1836]
No improvement. The joints are painful all the time.

Casebook entry: **2**/18

She has no appetite at all. She has had inflammation in her left eye for four days. Since then the joints have been less painful. The taste for eating charcoal is greater when she has flushes of blood to the head. [Exclamation mark in margin of text]

Repertory
(G) Tearing pains in the eyes. Sil.
She went to bed because of the pains and to avoid the bright light.

Prescription
Silica 30c (. /X) (!) in 15 [table]spoonfuls: every other evening 1 tablespoonful.

June 18th [1836]
Positively improved generally.
The hot flushes have threatened several times but failed to establish themselves.

For 36 hours she had red blotches on her cheeks, these have disappeared.

The pain in her wrists has gone.

There has been a singular improvement in her appearance and in her emotional disposition.

She has the desire to eat charcoal less often, but it's still there.

She is not at all melancholy any more and concerning this Hahnemann says that the mental symptoms are the most important.

Prescription
Silica 24c (. /VIII), 1 tablespoonful every other evening.

July 30th [1836]
Her right eye became red just once for a couple of days but there was no pain and it went quickly. The left eye was troubled for 5 days but there was no pain. She had a little inflammation and swelling in the gums. When she pressed them a little pus and blood came out of a little boil.

The gum – (symptom of Silica).

Her morale is excellent. In the past she has had a great deal of sadness and been cantankerous in nature.

She has had less desire for charcoal. It comes over her from time to time.

She has had pains in the joints, especially in the knees.

From time to time she has experienced a great rising dry heat which comes up from below to the head and sometimes ends in a sweat. She has had several periods of 2 or 3 days without having it and sometimes has had one or two a day.

Prescription
Silica 18c (. /VI) in 15 [table]spoonfuls, 1 tablespoonful to be taken every other evening.

April 12th 1837
Since the 8th January the desire to eat charcoal has completely gone (!!).

On the 2nd of March the pain returned violently to the right eye. It went on the 7th and came back on the 22nd, went again on the 23rd, came back on the 30th in the left eye and has not gone away since. She has constant lancinating pains in the corner of her eye. She has also had violent pains in the temple.

Sometimes when the left part of the gum swells, then the pain ceases.

But at present when her eye becomes painful again, then the gum goes down. Since the pain returned to her eye on January 8th the desire to eat charcoal has also returned, but she resists it perfectly well.
She has little appetite. She wakes with the pains.
She is very fearful of the day. She is fearful and distressed about her illness.

Repertory
(G) Sticking pains in corners of the eyes: Clem., Con., Ph., Tart.
(G) Worse bright light: Br., Caus., Clem., Ph., Sil., Ant.

Prescription
Ant. Cr. 30c (. /X) in 7 [table]spoonfuls [of water] and ½ table-spoonful of alcohol, 2 teaspoonfuls each evening and morning.

April 27th [1837]
The pain has left the left eye to lodge in the right. Now there are tearing pains in both eyes and the whites of both eyes are bloodshot.
She has hot flushes 20 or so times a day.
For sixteen years she has not been able to prevent herself from eating charcoal but this desire has completely disappeared since the 8th of January.

Repertory
(F) Hot flushes. Nux Vom.
She coughs and spits a great deal. Anxiety disturbs her in the night.
At present her eyes swell when they hurt (new).
She has no appetite.

Prescription
Nux Vom. 30c (. /X) in 7 tablespoonfuls, 2 teaspoonfuls three times daily.

Casebook entry: 2/41 (see facsimile, overleaf)

May 14th [1837]
(She has had Ant. Cr., Sil., Sil., Sil. Calc., Carb Veg., Cinn., Inhale Cic., HS, inhale Merc. Sol., Sulph., Sulph.)
She had Nux Vom. 30c (. /X) three times a day (2 teaspoonfuls).
The tearing pains have vanished from both eyes. She has not a single pain left.

The redness in the whites of the eyes has passed little by little. There only remain the hot flushes which have been rising to her face 8 to 10 times a day since March. Four times so far today, twice yesterday.

While she is lying in bed she is completely well but when she gets up in the morning she experiences swelling of the eyes and limbs. All that goes when she moves around.

Her appetite has come back a little. She no longer thinks of charcoal; she hardly coughs or spits anymore. She sleeps well for four to six hours without anxiety. No longer makes a rattling sound when she breathes in. She only wants open air and is much worse for being near the fire.

Prescription
Nux Vom. 24c (. /VIII) in 7 [table]spoonfuls, take 1 teaspoonful in the mornings, 2 in the evenings.

May 25th [1837]

She has had a fever for two days. She has had no more pain in her eyes.

The hot flushes continue, but are occurring only 3 or 4 times a day instead of 7 or 8.

She has no longer any swelling of her eyes or limbs.

Every month from the 18th to the 24th she suffers more with her eyes but at present there is no pain. From the 20th to the 24th of each month when the pain in the eyes is disposed to come back, the desire to eat charcoal takes hold of her a little and when her feet are cold the pain in the eyes also seems disposed to return.

She didn't have hot flushes last night in bed; she has no appetite.

The hot flushes with sweat come on unexpectedly.

Prescription
Hepar Sulph. 24c (. /VIII) in 14 [tablespoonfuls of water] and 1 of alcohol, 1 teaspoonful to be taken three times daily.

June 10th [1837]

She's well: she no longer has a fever.

Her eyes are good. Her left leg is swollen.

From time to time she has hot flushes . . . once or twice a day.

She has no longer any desire to eat charcoal. She has had a cold.

Her appetite is good enough; she no longer feels like crying.

Her knees are no longer swollen.

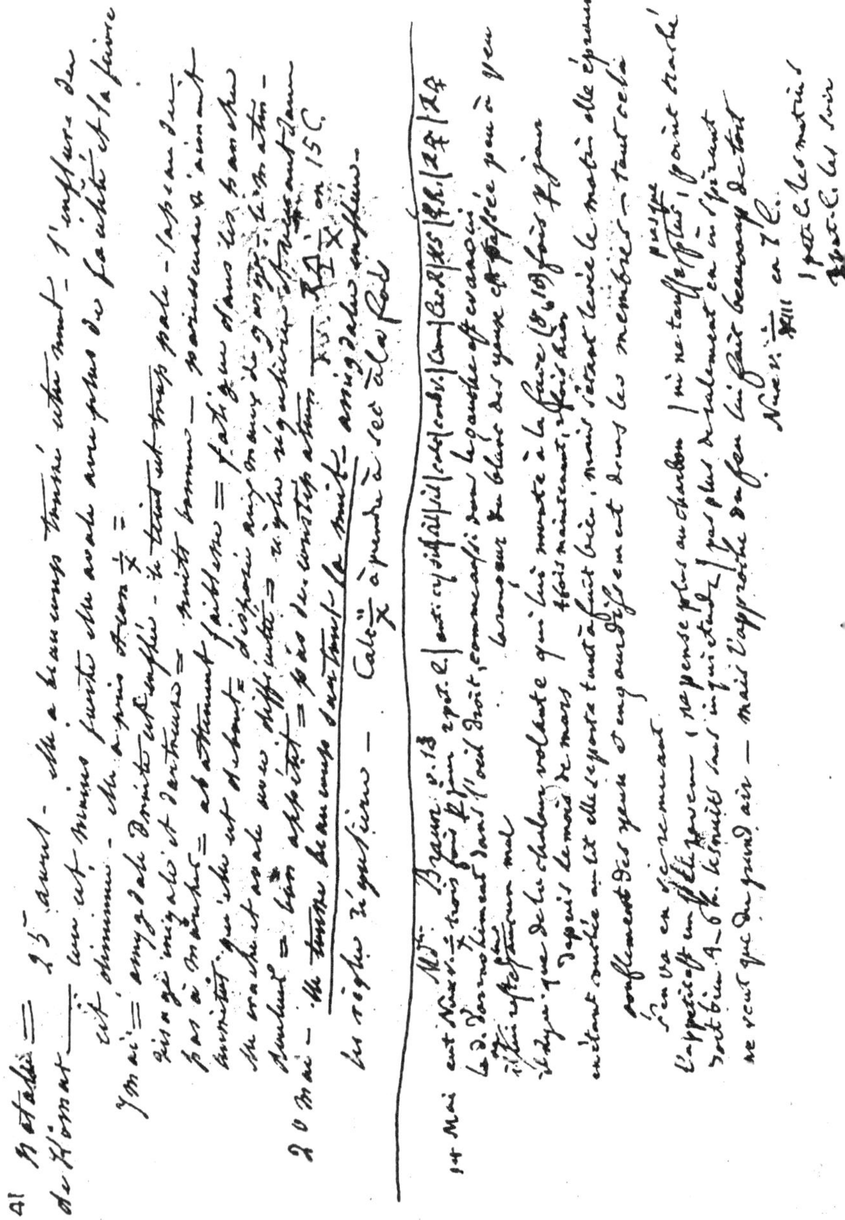

Mme Braun: See here the common practice of continuing a case on a space at the bottom of someone else's notes. The Hahnemanns must have been sure that Natalie de Komar had stopped coming and continued Mme Braun's case beneath hers. Note incidentally that Natalie de Komar's final recorded prescription is a rare example of a dry dose: Calc. ../X à prendre à sec à la fois

(Calc. Carb. 30c in a dry dose at the same time, presumably, as the Sulphur 30c prescribed daily in liquid doses). This section of Mme Braun's case is written by Samuel (first hand) and Melanie (second hand). Hahnemann refers at the beginning of the entry to page 13 of his casebook where he had last made notes about Mme Braun, and also reviews his earlier prescriptions to this patient.

Prescription
Hepar Sulph. 18c (. /VI) in 14 [tablespoonfuls of water] and 1½ of
alcohol, 1 teaspoonful to be taken 3 times daily.

Casebook entry: **2**/49

June 27 1837
On the 10th she had Hepar Sulph. 18c. The fever returned from the
23rd to the 25th (heat). On the 20th she had a malaise and sickness. If
she has no swelling (abscess) in her left upper gum, she has pain in the
left eye. The abscess has drained the swelling from the left eye six
times. The left eye gets more swollen at times and then the cheek
becomes less swollen. (Her leg is restored to health.)
The hot flushes had completely gone but returned on the 10th and have
gone since.
Nothing remains except the malaise: (head is heavy, legs feel broken).
Since the desire for charcoal has passed the desire for nourishing food
has got less.
Her knees are completely well.

Prescription
Hepar Sulph. 12c (. /IV) in 15 [tablespoonfuls of water], 3 of alcohol.
Take 1 teaspoonful in 6 tablespoonfuls of water each day.

July 27th [1837]
She's perfectly well.

July 27th 1838
She has been well during this year. No joint pain except once in
January. But her eyes have been a problem again on four occasions and
today she has conjunctivitis beneath the upper lid of the right eye.
She has had bleeding from the uterus once. She has had short-lived
leucorrhoea over the last five months (new), malaise and nausea. [She
has had no appetite for 2 months.]

Prescription
Not recorded but it must have been Sulphur 30c (see next appointment).

August 10th [1838]
(She has taken Sulphur 30c (. /X) in 15 tablespoonfuls of water, 1
tablespoonful 1–5 times daily.)

The discharge is less strong. The feeling of general malaise is less. Nausea less. She was ill for ten days then the general malaise and swelling of the mouth went away.

Prescription
Sulphur 24c (. /VIII) in 15 [tablespoonfuls of water] and 1 [of alcohol], 1 tablespoonful in a glass of water and take 1–6 teaspoonfuls daily.

August 24th [1838]
The pain in her eyes has gone. On the 18th her right gum was swollen. In the morning this gum was not swollen.
She has had hot flushes to the head. She gets very red suddenly. But they are less strong than usual.
The leucorrhoea has gone completely.
On the 21st the right eye became a little red but there was no pain.
Sleep a little agitated.
Less nausea and sickness.
Stools good.

Prescription
Sac lac in 15 [tablespoonfuls of water] and 1 [of alcohol], 1 table-spoonful in a glass of water, 1–6 teaspoonfuls daily.

September 14th [1838]
She has had no periods for five years. They came back a little 4 months ago. Before her period she had a heavy white discharge. She had another period two months ago. After it the hot flushes came back.
It's always at the time of her periods that the pain in the eyes appears to be on the point of coming back.
Every evening she has had pain in the lower jaw which continues through the night. In the mornings her gums are swollen and the pain passes during the day.

Prescription
Tinct. Hepar Sulph. 24c (. /VIII) in 15 [table]spoonfuls, 1 table-spoonful in a glass.

Casebook entry: **2**/73

Mme Braun's name is written here but nothing is entered beneath it.

Name: MUSARD, Philippe
Age 45, married
Occupation: Orchestra leader, musician, composer

Casebook entries: **4**/328–31, 333, 339–40, 353–6; **7**/67; **12**/23–4; **6**/380, 242–3, 293, 331

M. Musard's case illustrates almost all the characteristics of Hahnemann's prescribing practice and all the hazards of trying to represent it. The case is recorded on eighteen pages distributed through four different casebooks over a period of several years, from April 1837 till January 1842. Hahnemann and Melanie both took part in the writing of the case notes at different times.

Philippe Musard was one of the most famous band leaders of his day, one of the earliest musicians invited to conduct the Promenade Concerts when they were establised in London. He was an artiste, a man of temperament and imagination.

He continued to receive homeopathic treatment for many years after Hahnemann's death. When he had a stroke in 1860 he was attended by Charles Lethière, who had been Hahnemann's apothecary in later years and became Melanie's assistant after he qualified as a homeopathic doctor.

Musard referred many patients to the Hahnemanns and many members of his orchestra consulted them. His family were also prescribed for by Hahnemann and occasionally we find, in the margins of his case notes, notes of remedies or instructions sent home for them.

When he first visited Hahnemann he was suffering from recurrent attacks of severe abdominal pain. These were usually accompanied by mild fever and constipation and he felt better for passing stool. During the attacks he was breathless and had pain in his sides and various parts of his body. He also suffered from pain (often described as lancinating) and cracking or creaking in the knees, and his feet and legs often swelled up after walking.

In the first phase of his treatment the main concern seems to have been his abdominal pains. At first he seemed to do well on

homeopathic treatment, which consisted mainly of prescriptions of Sulphur 30c in various different dilutions of water or water and alcohol, interrupted only once by an instruction to inhale Bryonia while at Hahnemann's house when he had a cold and a cough.

After a few months, however, on May 23rd, 1837, the prescription seems to have caused an aggravation of some itching on the scrotum which he had had for many years (20 or 27) and so, after waiting for a little while, on June 22nd, Hahnemann prescribed Ambra Grisea 30c in response to the worsening of the itching. This, while helping the itching, seems to have provoked a urethral discharge, fever and disturbed sleep; an 'attack' threatened but did not materialise.

After this things settled down, but not completely, and Musard seems to have reported on July 18th that he had not been so well since 'the little relapse caused by the Ambra'. However, he did eventually recover from the relapse and Hahnemann continued patiently with his initial prescription of Sulphur for several weeks, occasionally using inhalations of Nux Vomica if the pains were particularly severe – ('Whenever he experiences a little more pain during the day he is to suspend the evening teaspoonful [of Sulphur] and take Nux instead') – prescribing inhalations of Causticum and Bryonia when he got a sore throat, reverting to Sulphur as his base remedy when the throat cleared up.

In September 1837 Hahnemann began to prescribe Lycopodium, apparently in response to the clearer emergence of pains in the liver area (after repertorising this symptom). He prescribed Lycopodium 30c followed by Lycopodium 24c, with sac lac introduced for a few days.

There was then a gap of a few weeks in the treatment, a gap during which it appears that Musard had been away in the country. When he returned to Paris in October 1837 it was to report a return of the abdominal pains, which were always worse in Paris than in the country. At this stage in the treatment Hahnemann used a number of different remedies in an attempt to get to grips with Musard's pains. He repertorised various symptoms and prescribed, successively, Sabadilla, Cannabis, Conium and Opium before, in November 1837 going on to Sulphur 18c, his last prescription of Sulphur having been 24c some months earlier. He stayed with the daily Sulphur for several weeks, 18c followed by 12c interspersed with the occasional inhaled dose of Nux Vomica, and by February 1838 Musard seemed to have improved quite considerably.

Indeed, from February 1838 he seemed not to have had any need of Hahnemann for over a year, except when he got an acute sore throat from travelling on the outside of a railway carriage in September 1838. This was treated at first with Belladonna 30c and then Hahnemann went back to the top of the Sulphur scale (having reached 3c in February shortly before the break in treatment), interspersing daily liquid doses of that with inhaled doses of Nux Vomica for a few days.

In May of the following year, 1838, Musard returned with a recurrence of the abdominal pains, breathlessness and weakness. By this time Hahnemann had begun to use the higher centesimal potencies and so began his treatment of this new phase with Sulphur 190c, using other remedies as indicated in the lower potencies: Hepar Sulph. 30c, Lycopodium 18c (the last dose of Lycopodium was 24c over eighteen months previously) and Cinnabar 30c. Hahnemann then prescribed Hepar Sulph. 85c and one dose of Ignatia, and continued treatment with this even while Musard apparently went to London for a while. The musician seemed to improve on this treatment and when he came back a few weeks later was prescribed Kali Carb., needing nothing further for several months. At this point the records of his appointments are not always made sequentially, so it is difficult to pick one's way around his case.

However, he seems not to have come for nearly a year between October 1839 and August 1840 and by then, in this next phase of treatment, he was concerned mainly with attacks of gout and goutty rheumatism in his hands. This became his main preoccupation, since his abdominal pains – his initial complaint – were not so bothersome by then and only occasionally returned. Hahnemann initially prescribed Hepar Sulph. for the gouty symptoms, along with advocating plunging the feet in well water for a few minutes daily, but it was eventually Rhus Tox. which was successful in clearing up the pain.

A couple of months later the abdominal pains returned and Hahnemann again reverted to the base Sulphur, using the LM potency for the first time with Musard, Sulphur LM 10 (10/oo). He also asked him occasionally to inhale Lycopodium and eventually to take Lycopodium 30c in liquid doses, and once or twice, Belladonna 30c. On May 17th he repeated the prescription of Sulphur in LM 10, on May 29th he went to LM 7 and because Musard was in severe pain he then gave him Camphor 30c in liquid, whereupon the pains calmed down.

The rheumatic pains seem by then to have become more troublesome in his hands than in his feet, and Hahnemann tried the previously effective Rhus Tox. Apparently this was not successful because Musard resorted to taking herbal colchicum without asking permission! Melanie noted frostily: 'Suddenly the pains in the liver and intestines came back.' Hahnemann then proceeded to prescribe Hepar Sulph. LM 5 which seemed to improve things a bit.

At that point Musard's gouty pains in the foot returned; they were quickly palliated with Rhus Tox. but returned if he stopped taking the remedy.

Hahnemann once again tried to get to grips with the case by prescribing successive doses of Hepar Sulph., now going up the scale from LM 5 to LM 6 to LM 7, until the pains become very localised in the big toe and at that point cleared up on Guaiacum 30c.

Then the abdominal pains threatened again and were cleared up with Rhus Tox., whereupon the rheumatic pains in the hands reappeared temporarily until he stopped taking the remedy. He was then left with slight abdominal pains and Hahnemann returned to the Hepar Sulph., now in LM 8.

After this, and till the end of the record of his treatment, Hahnemann seems to have resorted to treating the on top symptoms with the old low centesimal potencies decanted into two and sometimes three glasses, with teaspoonful doses being taken from the last, because Musard appears to have become even more sensitive to remedies by then than he was at the outset of his treatment.

Musard tended to visit Hahnemann about once a week when he was in active treatment, or even more frequently when he was in the grip of an acute, but this pattern, like that of many other of Hahnemann's patients, was often interrupted by his absences from Paris. Not only did he have a country residence in Auteuil (where he eventually became mayor), but he was also sometimes away in London conducting the Promenade Concerts. While in London he was sometimes prescribed for by Dr Quin, though without conspicuous success, and sometimes by Hahnemann through letters.

Musard was quite a difficult patient to treat. He was anxious about his health, not to say a supreme hypochondriac. A lot of his symptoms appear to have been brought on by nerves – he always seems worse when working hard, especially when performing, and he was always worse in Paris than when relaxing at his country home at Auteuil. His anxiety also made him difficult to treat. He was quickly despondent after any setback, such as the relapse after Ambra Grisea. He also seems to have easily aggravated from the remedies. On August 4th he inhaled Nux a little too strongly and got a sore throat. On September 4th, taking Sulphur three times daily also caused an aggravation.

We see Hahnemann trying his best to avoid this by several methods.

He tried reducing the dose, advised the succussion of intermediate glasses, using a second or third glass, or using olfaction. Hahnemann started decanting into a glass very early with Musard and had soon proceeded to make use of two and three glasses. On September 18th 1837, Lycopodium 24c was decanted into three glasses. On November 18th 1837, after an aggravation from taking three tablespoonfuls daily, Musard was instructed to take only one daily. Inhalation was used frequently. (Bryonia was inhaled in response to the acute respiratory problem which came on in the middle of chronic treatment of the abdominal pains.) There was also much use of sac lac.

As in other cases, we see the characteristic alternation in the resonant frequency of the remedies used. In the early days there seems to have been an alternation between the use of remedies by mouth for the ongoing treatment and inhalation for acutes. Later we see the alternation between the use of higher centesimal potencies for the ongoing treatment, and lower centesimal potencies, taken in liquid or inhaled, for the acutes; and in the later years, the beginnings of the alternation between LM (globule) potencies for the ongoing treatment and the centesimal for acutes.

April 1st [1837]
He is in fairly good health. He has had scabies and dry scurfy skin in the past.

Eight months ago in August he had feelings of suffocation, difficulty breathing, followed by an attack of colicky pain, beginning mildly and increasing: a dull continuous pain which spread throughout his whole body and was followed by black and sad thoughts and continual drowsiness. Pressure relieved the pain and he was better when he lay down on his belly on the floor. The pain affected all his faculties and made him morose and bad-tempered, wanting to die. The pain increased slowly over four or five days and then diminished in the same way. It begins at a little point in the navel and spreads out slowly, growing little by little, and eventually encompassing the whole belly, then the pain becomes terrible and he has continuous straining and constipation: when he is able to pass stool he is cured.

(At the beginning of the attack a poultice was applied, this was followed by leeches and finally purgatives: he had opium morning and evening. He has not had an attack for three months.)

The attacks usually last eight days. He is breathless before and after them. During the period of breathlessness he can digest his food quite well. His breathing is always restricted.

He always has a little breathlessness but it is much stronger 24 hours before the attacks of colic, which have not changed their character.

(He has taken syrups to cleanse himself.)

Cold brings on and increases the attacks, and when he talks a lot the pain comes back. He is never completely free from the abdominal pains.

He had a scab on the inside of his thigh which disappeared of its own accord at the time when the colicky pains started. It has occasionally reappeared in the intervals between the attacks.

He has had three bad boils which were cut open and then discharged: the colicky illness came on after this.

He has not slept with his wife for eight months.

He does not drink coffee or tea or undiluted wine.

Prescription

Sulphur 30c (. /X)

Put one drop of Sulphur 30c in a mixture of equal parts of water and spirits of wine. Put 400 drops of this mixture into a glass, succuss it 5 times, then take one drop and put it in 2 tablespoonfuls [of liquid] into a second glass. From this take 2 teaspoonfuls three times daily.

Charged three hundred francs.

April 5th [1837]

Yesterday he had the slight abdominal pains which presage the bigger ones. His health has been perfect for three days; since April 1st. His pains came back at exactly the same time! Today he has very feeble pains: the nights are worse than the days. He feels as if he wants to pass a stool but he can't. When he has the pain it always seems to him that he would be better if he could pass a stool and he is in fact immediately better whenever he does so.

Prescription

He is to put one drop of the medicine in 2 tablespoonfuls of water in a second glass. In the morning he is to shake the glass five times and then take 1 teaspoonful only, throwing the rest away.

April 7th 1837

He has taken one teaspoonful twice a day and the pains have not increased, rather they have lessened and changed in some way: they are not so gripping as they were before. Sometimes they go away and in their place he experiences a tickling sensation to the side of his navel (*Theridion*). The pains sometimes come every quarter of an hour. He's sleeping and eating well and his digestion is good. Breath is bad, smells fetid and stagnant. He is only half as constipated. He has pain in the ribs, little general pain. He has all the symptoms of the attack but in miniature.

He has no longer so much breathlessness: he can breathe comfortably.

Prescription
Continue 3 times a day.

April 18th [1837]

He's very well. He has continued the drops of Sulphur shaken as usual. *Stool is always good. He's not so irritable. There is still a fetid odour if he has any pain.*

His knee still cracks especially in the evening. He sometimes gets tingling and tremors around the knee.

He's still always thirsty.

He's taken 2 teaspoonfuls at a time three times a day from the mixture with the 2 tablespoonfuls.

His feet get swollen after walking.

His lower ribs hurt if he talks a lot.

Prescription
Continue with the remedy.

(Beneath this entry is a note in SH's hand prescribing Sulphur 30c for Mme Musard's condition – itching at night.)

April 20th [1837]

He's very well: appetite and digestion are good. He feels stronger, his legs are still swollen but less so.

He's itchy, especially in the evening. He occasionally has pains during the day around his neck and belly.

He has the lancinating pains in his knee on movement but less than before.

He's dreaming at present, something he never used to do: he dreams of his household. Previously he dreamed in a similar way.

His abdominal pains are still of the same nature but not nearly so strong.

He feels the pain returning but it seems to have diminished.

He has a stool every day without straining.

Prescription
He has continued to take 3 times daily 2 teaspoonfuls from 1 drop
prepared with two tablespoonfuls of water.

April 27th [1837]
Stool every day, good appetite, nights good.
Swelling of legs even less, walking a lot.
Itching less; he feels no more pain in the lower abdomen.
No lancinating pains in the right knee during the day, (cracking still),
only in the evening in bed at 11 or 12 p.m., ever decreasing.

Prescription
Continue 3 times daily to take 2 tablespoonfuls prepared with 1 drop.

May 5th [1837]
On April 29th he went to bed in the evening at the time of the attacks:
he was shivering and his skin was burning hot. He then sweated a lot,
soaking the mattress, till morning. There was no pain but he was very
weak and looked terrible. This weakness lasted 2 days but there was no
pain or constipation and no change in his morale.
His character has become better in general!
He has had a good appetite. Sleeps very well; less thirsty; his dreams
have nearly stopped.
Still very chilly, great difficulty getting his cold feet warm.
For at least 5 or 6 days he has not had a lancinating pain in the knee
even in the evenings; the swelling in his feet has almost gone.
He's still irascible.

Prescription
He is to succuss the two glasses 10 times.

May 12th [1837]
Yesterday he felt very drowsy – he usually has this drowsiness before
and during an attack. It is now the time of the attack.
He thinks he has a cold: he's coughing a little.
He has stiffness and pain in the legs and arms; heaviness in the limbs; a
little pain in the left ribs, pain in the sternum on breathing; throat
sensitive on swallowing; a little pain in the sides and abdomen; sleep
heavy and agitated.

Prescription
Inhale Bryonia here.

Casebook entry: **4**/330

May 13th [1837]
He's much better with regard to the stiffness and in the limbs.
This morning he had two liquid stools with a little colic. He slept better.
When he breathes deeply he can still feel the point on the sternum but less; the cough has gone; less heaviness and little or no drowsiness. Throat nearly recovered; still a little difficulty on breathing; less pain in ribs and belly.

Prescription
Not recorded.

May 23rd [1837]
Perfectly alright. He has a little red rash in the inside of his nose. He gets this when he uses too much tobacco. Pain in the knee has not returned . . . he only feels a mild sensation.
He's eating, drinking and sleeping perfectly well.
He has had good stools.
His appetite is reasonable and he eats with pleasure.

Prescription
Put 1 drop from 400 drops in 6 teaspoonfuls of water: take two teaspoonfuls of this mixture three times daily.

June 10th [1837]
The itchiness is back very strongly.
Little colicky pains from time to time, stools regular.
He has had some itchiness on the scrotum (for twenty years) and it's been aggravated since May 23rd. After he had scratched scabs formed.

Prescription
Not recorded.

June 22nd [1837]
Itching (of the genitals) has come back with great strength (pinkish scabs).
The pain in the knee has completely gone.

Repertory
(G) Itching in the scrotum: Ambr., Cocc., Caust., Iod., Bar., Pet., Rhod.
(G) Dry scabs in the scrotum: Dulc., Pet., Tox. (Sore throat previously.)

Prescription
Ambra Grisea 30c (. /X), 1 drop in 15 tablespoonfuls [of water] and 1¹/₂ of alcohol: 1 tablespoonful morning and night for 4 days and then sac lac for 3 days.

June 27th [1837]
The itching in the scrotum (which he's had for 27 years (sic)) has diminished, (ambr!) but when he urinates his urethral canal smarts and there is a light discharge from the penis; he has breathlessness; abdominal pains. He is straining, gets one hard stool. Sleep agitated.

Prescription
He is to stop taking the sac lac and is to put 1 drop [of the Ambra Grisea] in 6 tablespoonfuls of water. Today he is to take 1 teaspoonful at 4 o'clock. Tomorrow 1 teaspoonful from it three times. The day after tomorrow, 2 teaspoonfuls.

June 29th [1837]
After having taken the drop on the 27th he felt better again, he was able to eat dinner quite well. In the evening he was well.
On the 28th he had stiffness all day which improved in the evening. On going to bed he shivered violently and sweated profusely until 4 a.m.
Continuous restlessness in his limbs with internal and visible trembling, sometimes of the whole of his body, sometimes of one limb only with sudden seizures and sensations like electric shocks. At 4 a.m., when the sweat had stopped, he felt no better. On previous occasions, after the feverish effect just described, the abdominal pains would take hold immediately and begin to increase, but this time they have not done so.
Yawning and stretching of the limbs. Before this he had only one such episode of sweating with very hot skin.
He has general stiffness with bruised pain in all the limbs.
Pains in the sides as if he were tired.
Sense of pressure in the sternum, pains as if the bones were bruised. At present (9 a.m.), yawning and stretching, drowsiness without being able to sleep.

169

Prescription
1 drop in 6 tablespoonfuls of water: take one teaspoonful every half hour.

Casebook entry: **4**/331

July 4th [1837]
He has a little lump on the top of his penis which is inflamed all the time and there is lancinating pain (old symptom). No further difficulty in urinating.

Prescription
Not recorded.

July 10th [1837]
For the past three days he has mixed the 1 drop in 3 tablespoonfuls of liquid and taken doses from it three times.
The itching on the scrotum has come back, but to a lesser degree.
Appetite was less for 7 days but has been better for the last three.
The lump on the penis has abscessed and vanished.
He's sleeping quite well.

Prescription
1 drop in 6 coffee spoonfuls (tablespoonfuls crossed out).

July 18th [1837]
For the last 2 or 3 days has had little abdominal pains.
He has had little nervous twitches and tremors in his arm and the joints of his hands.
His abdomen is sensitive to touch.
Sometimes has stiffness and drowsiness.
Generally, since the little relapse caused by the Ambra, his health has not been as good as it was before.
Sometimes some breathlessness or feelings of suffocation.
The itching of the scrotum is strong.
No difficulty in urinating.
Pains in the belly as if he wanted to pass a stool.
Drowsiness by day.

Prescription
Inhale Nux Vom. 30c (/X).
Tomorrow inhale Nux Vom. 24c (/VIII).

After tomorrow take 1 drop in 6 tablespoonfuls stirred 20 times, and take 1 teaspoonful from that mixture 3 times daily.

August 1st [1837]
He only gets the little pains from time to time for a few hours or more in a whole day.
Bowels clear, sleeping and eating well. He's only drinking water.

Prescription
Sulphur 24c (. /VIII) in 500 drops.

Whenever he experiences a little more pain during the day he is to suspend the evening teaspoonful and inhale Nux instead.

August 4th [1837]
He inhaled the Nux a little too strongly. He has a sore throat, perhaps a little chill. When he swallows it hurts as if there were a scratch (*a swelling*).
He has had pains in his throat at other times; sensation of pressure in the throat on the left.
Yesterday morning and this morning he only took one teaspoonful.
He's still a bit stiff.

Prescription
He is to take the medicine twice daily and come back to see me.

August 5th [1837]
Sore throat increased, pain on the left side. When he swallows salt water he has a stinging sensation (pain as if scratched).

Repertory
(G) Pain in the throat on swallowing.

Continual salivation – this sore throat is an old malady which he has had for 6 years; it comes back every year.
He feels generally unwell.
He feels no pain in the lower abdomen or the knees.
He still has the itching in the scrotum.

Prescription
Inhale Causticum.

August 6th [1837]
He inhaled once more after dinner. Then he had an attack: first shivering and then very hot; then he started to sweat (normal fever of these sicknesses) then he slept well until the morning.

Prescription
Nothing.

August 7th [1837]
Throat is doing very well; there is only a little discomfort on the left side.

Prescription
Inhale Causticum – less strongly.

August 8th [1837]
His throat is doing well; he still has the grazed sensation a little when he talks too much.

August 24th [1837]
Yesterday he was weak in the stomach, had constriction in the chest due to vexations.

Prescription
He is to inhale Bryonia for three days.

Casebook entry: **4**/333

September 4th [1837]
For the three days when he inhaled Bryonia he was well, but then three days afterwards he started again on the Sulphur 24c, 1 drop diluted in 500 drops, 3 teaspoonfuls daily for 2–3 days and since then the severe pains have come back in the lower abdomen and the suffocative feelings in his chest when he breathes in deeply.
(Stools good), appetite bad, no taste for meat, vegetables, still likes milk.
He has a sense of pressure in the ribs and continuous gripping pains (colicky).
(In his sleep at night he keeps moving about, is agitated.)
If he presses his lower abdomen with his hands the pain dies down.
He has a little burning in the chest (Ars.).

172

Prescription
Finish inhaling the Nux Vom. tomorrow and the morning after and then sac lac.

September 11th [1837]
He's not well. There's always something to annoy him.
In his right side he has soreness, burning and bruised pain.
His dreams are troubled and he's impatient in them.
Bitter taste in mouth, fatigue, drowsiness.
When he has the severe pains they are always worse on the right side.
He believes that beating time with his hand and foot has caused this aggravation.

Repertory
(G) Burning pain in the liver: Carb., Clem.
(G) Bruised pain in the liver: Carb., Clem., Lycop.

The internal pains make him depressed.
He has little colicky pains from time to time.
A lot of yawning.

Prescription
Lycopodium 30c (. /X) in 20 [tablespoonfuls of water] and 3 of alcohol: he is to put 1 teaspoonful in a glass of water and take 1 teaspoonful today, 2 tomorrow, 3 the day after tomorrow.

September 13th [1837]
His heart is beating very slowly (new).
Agitated nights. No stool yesterday or today.
He has weakness in his chest (pit of the stomach).
The pain in the right side low down (liver?) is better.
During these pains he is always drowsy.
Pain in the lower abdomen which continues to be aggravated by pressure (bruised pain). A little colic makes him go to stool.
Cannot stay a long time in the same place.
A lot of yawning.
Sometimes when he bends down his pulse becomes very slow.
He no longer has bad breath.

Repertory
(G) Bruised pain in the belly: Amm., Caust., Mur. Mag.

(G) Evacuation obstructed: Con., Cact.
(G) Desires sleep: Con.

Prescription
Before giving Conium:
Today take sac lac in 4 tablespoonfuls for 2 days. (Or Cinnabar?)

September 15th [1837]

The pain increased but he's not suffering as much as at other times.
He complains of a great weakness in the hypochondrium (Dig., Ign., Pet., Nitr., Croc.) and of a great sensitivity to touch of the genitals, ribs and kidneys.
The night of the 13/14 was bad. Yesterday he had little or no stool.
Better night 14/15, this morning one little stool. The pain is less and there's less drowsiness. Yesterday evening he had a headache as if squeezed in a vice. He is less restless and less inclined to yawn. During the night he has to turn over 100 times: he likes to sleep on the hard floor.
What is his pulse?
?HS, ?Cinn.

Prescription
Carry on with sac lac.

Casebook entry: **4**/339 (continued from **4**/333)

September 18th [1837]

Pains in abdomen and kidneys are less strong.
General weakness; momentary throbbing throughout the whole body; his pulse goes slower suddenly and then the throbbing starts heavy and slow. It happens often of its own accord.
Still gets little feelings of breathlessness but without palpitations in the heart. The feeling of suffocation comes on at the times when he is not digesting food well.
Has a sensation of emptiness in the body: (Ant. Cr., Cocc., Coloc., Euph., Guia., Merc., Nat. Mur., Oleand., Sab., Sep.).
Regular pressure on the abdomen does him good but sudden pressure is painful.
The scabs don't itch at all. This is what happens when his belly is bad.
Has slept better.

Prescription
Lycopodium 24c (. /VIII) in 20 [tablespoonfuls of water and] 3 of alcohol, succuss twice and put 1 teaspoonful in a glass of water: take 1 teaspoonful from this each morning after stirring.

October 30th [1837]

The morning after he left the country air (in Auteuil) and came back to his old home in Paris the pain in the lower abdomen started again. He has been at the Rue d'Alger for four days and his whole body is affected. There's always something in the abdomen which makes him anxious. He always feels a kind of constriction in his chest.
He has a scraping pain in the liver. Pain from pressure. (Sabad., Sel., Tab.). Always during the pains he has a false need for stool. He does not yet have a stool everyday. In Paris his sleep is always agitated.

Repertory
(F) He stretches his limbs: Amm., Caust., Graph., Guai., Nat. Mur., Nux Vom., Oleand., Petrol, Plat., Puls., Rut., Sabad., Sen., Sep., Staph., Sulph.
(F) Always thirsty while he has the pains: Coloc., Staph., Sars., Caust., Cann., Sabad.

Prescription
Sabadilla 30c (. /X) in 20 [tablespoonfuls of water and] 1 of alcohol: 1 teaspoonful in a glass of water and 1 teaspoonful from that every morning.
(First wrote Sabad., then Cann., then went back to Sabad.)
Next Cann.

November 5th [1837]

On the 31st he took the teaspoonful and he was a little better.
On the first of November he had more pain in the lower abdomen and the pain ascended. He had trembling of the legs and the arms the first days, today he feels on edge.
After that he had more pain in his chest (stomach) than his abdomen.
At the moment his breathing is difficult. He cannot get to sleep and he has had very restless sleep over the last three nights. On the third day he had two liquid stools which burnt him in the anus. Everyday he has one stool. The pit of his stomach hurts him when pressed and the feeling of oppression increases.
Morale is not worse.

He is less thirsty. The burning in his chest has stopped.
He is always wanting to stretch out.
Has a little appetite.

Prescription
He is to take Cannabis for no more than two days and three doses of
sac lac daily after that.

Casebook entry: **4**/340 (see facsimile, overleaf)

November 6th [1837]

(Bad). He's suffering in the stomach and bowels. Yesterday he had no pain in the bowels.

Yesterday he conducted the orchestra and it is possible that that has tired him and caused the pain to increase.

He has not suffered as much while he has been having homeopathic treatment.

All his limbs are stiff which is usual when he is in a lot of pain.

November 7th [1837]

(Less pain). This night was better than the last.

Pains in the limbs, stiffness everywhere, pains in the legs but above all in the stomach.

He has come himself today, yesterday he could not have come; he is not as bad as yesterday.

False desire for stool but less strong than other times. This symptom always accompanies the crisis state.

Irregular beating of the heart.

He rarely has the stinging pains.

Repertory
(G) Bruised pain in the bowels: Con., Cocc., Coloc., HS, Led., Ran.,
Rut., Samb., Sep., Stram., Verat.
(F) Cramping pain in the bowels: Cop., Ran., Tox., Ac. Sulph., (Cin.,
Con., Nux Mosch.)
(Even when touched. Cina.)

For these two days he took only sac lac.
Constantly moving about.
(F) Sensation of emptiness in the lower abdomen and chest: Ant.,
Cocc., Coloc., Euph., Guai., Merc. Sol., Nat. Mur., Oleand., Sars., Sep.,
Stann.

(F) Tearing pains in limbs and joints: Sep.
(F) Drowsiness: Con., Cinn., Coloc., Sep.

Has no longer any itching even in the genitals.

Prescription
!! *Conium 30c (. /X) in 15 [table]spoonfuls [of water] and 1 of alcohol.*
Put 1 tablespoonful in one glass of water and take one teaspoonful
from this every two days.
(Con.!! got rid of pains.)

November 9th [1837]
The pains in kidneys and joints are much less.
He's taking everything more calmly than before; he still has to move
around often.
He's always fearful about the spot under his right ribs: he feels a little
burning there at times. Still constipated, an enema has done nothing.
Even at night little or no sleep but drowsiness.
He has no ideas. (Yesterday morning he felt better for the first time.)
He is less thirsty, but has no appetite. The breathlessness is much
diminished.

Prescription
Inhale Opium this evening and tomorrow at 9 a.m. take the [liquid]
medicine: 1 small teaspoonful at 1 p.m. and 5p.m.

November 11th [1837]
The night of the 9th/10th was bad. When he got up the pains were in
general much greater than they had been the previous day.
With great effort one very small stool, hard, moulded. At midday abun-
dant stool and he was left with a weakness of the stomach, ribs and
kidneys.
A little breathlessness, general weakness, tired pains in the legs.
The feeling of suffocation continues to increase. Little pains above and
around the ribs sometimes like stabbing or mild smarting.
After having dined with a reasonably good appetite he had a stool.
In the evening the pain and breathlessness continued. The night of
the 11th he was restless and his sleep was interrupted by the pains.
Towards morning sleep was peaceful enough; the pains a little less
strong.

M. Musard: Written by Melanie (first hand) and Samuel (second hand). The success of Conium is noted in the margin. There is a clear instruction to inhale Opium that evening and to take a liquid medicine twice the next day.

Prescription
Continue to take 1 teaspoonful three times daily today and tomorrow.

November 13th [1837]
A stool every day.

November 17th [1837]
He had to rehearse some pieces of music yesterday evening which perhaps tired him (*and put him into a bad mood*). He says he feels the return of an attack is imminent: he has a lot of breathlessness, lassitude, stiffness in the limbs and pain in the sides: the early symptoms of an attack.
Today less stool than yesterday.

Prescription
Sulphur 18c (. /VI) in 20 [tablespoonfuls of water] and 1 [of alcohol], 1 tablespoonful in a glass of water and take 1 teaspoonful up to 3 times daily.

Casebook entry: **4**/353

November 18th [1837]
Yesterday he started to take the Sulphur 18c up to 3 times daily: this morning the pains in the lower abdomen have come back.
At night the same weakness of the limbs returned. He cannot hold himself upright without trembling.
The approach of his wife makes him tremble.
Weakness at the bottom of the back.
The return of these pains was preceded by an attack of breathlessness which has passed since then.

Prescription
He is to take only 1 teaspoonful.

November 20th [1837]
He hasn't had a stool for 4/5 days. No appetite. Pains have been a little less so he's slept better this night than the last. Pains especially in the abdomen.
He can't stay in bed more than 15–20 minutes; he walks about, sits up and tosses about.
He has no thirst. He takes milk in the morning, soup at dinner.

Prescription
He is to take a second teaspoonful today, and three tomorrow and after tomorrow let me have a report.

November 22nd [1837]
Has not improved for several days. However he seems not to be suffering as much because he can remain drowsy.
He gets angry over nothing.
No appetite at all.
Still no stool, a lot of wind last night; no more breathlessness.
Little stabbing sensations in the depths of the abdomen.
He's very distressed and presumes that he will die from the same disease as his father.
Sleeping 5, 6 hours.
Skin of chest and abdomen very . . . [line not finished]
The pains return at longer intervals.

Repertory
(G) Touchy disposition: Anac., Calc., Cann., Iod., Lyc., Samb., Sen., Sep., Sulph.
(G) Impatience: Dros., Dulc., Ign., Ipec., Merc. Sol., Nat. Mur., Nat. Sulph., Zinc.
(G) Indignation: Acon., Amm., Anac., Aur., Bry., Canth., Caps., Cinn., Crot., Cupr., Kali., Led., Mur. Ac., Natr., Nit., Nux Vom., Oleand., Ptl., Ran., Sabad., Sen., Sep., Stann., Stront.
(G) Anxiety about Health: Sep.
(G) Sensitivity of skin to touch: Ang., Ant. Cr., Camph., Cina, Colch., Laur., (Nux Vom.); Oleand., Puls., Sabad., Spig. (Chin., Coff.)

Prescription
He is to continue to take three teaspoonfuls daily.

November 23rd [1837]
No stool but sleep a little deeper.
Yesterday (sensitivity) in the back beneath the shoulder.
Breaking wind a lot, wants no solid food, is taking some soup.
He does not look too bad, is not haggard.

Prescription
He is to take 4 teaspoonfuls daily.
He has had: Sulphur 18c, Op. inhaled, Con., Sabad., Lyc., Lyc., Nux Vom. inhaled, Ambr., Bryonia inhaled, Sulphur 30c.

November 24th 1837
He had a good motion at midday. He has eaten and slept well.
Fewer pains in the lower abdomen today.

Prescription
He is to continue with 4 teaspoonfuls daily.

November 29th [1837]
The breathlessness has gone.
He has only a few pains in the lower abdomen.
Stool is good, he sleeps quite well.
But he is very thirsty.

Prescription
Inhale Nux Vom. 24c (. /VIII) here and then continue with the 4 tea-
spoonfuls [of Sulphur].

November 30th [1837]
He was well yesterday and today but this afternoon at 4 p.m. he
complained a little of breathlessness.

Casebook entry: **4**/354

December 4th [1837]
The breathlessness has not continued and the little abdominal pains
have not increased though they are still there. This is the first time that
the breathlessness has not increased once it has started and the same
applies to the abdominal pains. As soon as his feet get cold the pains
increase.
He's had good motions. Ordinarily he's always constipated with the
pains.
The foot sweat has vanished since he has been ill.

Prescription
Sulphur 12c (. /IV) in 20 tablespoonfuls of water, 2 of alcohol, put
1 tablespoonful in a glass of water and take three teaspoonfuls the first
few days.

December 15th [1837]
The night of Tuesday to Wednesday he vomited after having eaten, had
4 liquid stools and then great weakness in the knees.

Nevertheless, he is getting better and better: the pains in the abdomen are fewer.

December 26th [1837]
He's eating with pleasure; feels well, regular stools.
He's sleeping well. He dreams infrequently in small snatches.
When he goes to bed his stomach rumbles. No pain in the abdomen.
He is better than he was during the relapse.
No more suffocation.

Prescription
Sulphur 12c (. /IV) in 20 [tablespoonfuls of water] and 2 [of alcohol], put 1 tablespoonful in a glass of water and take 1 teaspoonful three times [a day].

January 25th [1838]
He's quite well but his hands are still cold.

February 5th [1838]
He has been conducting the dances for many nights now and compos-ing at home.
Yesterday he had a pain in the liver.

Prescription
Sulphur 3c (. /I) in 20 [tablespoonfuls of water and] 2 [of alcohol]. Put 1 tablespoonful in a glass of water and take 1–2 teaspoonfuls from that.

[Prescription of Hepar Sulph. for his son added to the text]
[There is a gap in the record of treatment until the following entry.]

September 14th 1838
He has been travelling on the outside of the railway carriage and has got a violent sore throat; he cannot swallow, has an obstructed throat, no fever, no great thirst. He is talking with difficulty as if he had a blocked throat.
Yesterday during the day he had a few very slight pains in his bowels which did not last.

Prescription
Belladonna 30c (. /X)

September 15th [1838]

He is better. He has been eating with much greater ease. This morning he was swallowing saliva. He is constipated – the pain prevents him from resting properly: he has had to move about, but he has slept.

He has still some difficulty in swallowing his saliva: he complains of a generalised pain in the chest, the stomach and the kidneys, not in one place particularly, like a strong pressure.

It seems to him that if he could have a stool he would be well (he only had a little stool yesterday and nothing the day before). Yesterday evening he had a little fever, felt hot and cold but it didn't last long.

Prescription

Sulphur 30c (. /X) in 8 [tablespoonfuls of water] and 1 [of alcohol]. Put 1 tablespoonful from one glass of water into a second glass and take 1 teaspoonful from that.

September 16th [1838]

Yesterday he was well; the pains in the belly are not worse. He is a little less drowsy.

He is hungry and the sore throat prevents him from eating bread. He is dribbling saliva because he cannot swallow; he cannot speak easily.

Prescription

Inhale Nux Vom. 30c (. /X) now and before noon.

Casebook entry: **4/355**

September 17th [1838]

Yesterday his throat was very good after inhaling Nux Vom. In the evening he was only a little better, in the morning a little more so, but today he has eaten better than yesterday morning; his pain is much better.

Today he has had a little hard stool.

Yesterday he was a little less drowsy.

He is still spitting out a lot of saliva.

He has slept, though restlessly. His morale is better.

Prescription

Inhale Nux Vom. once more.

September 18th [1838]
*His gums are still a little swollen and on swallowing he still has pain
and soreness.*
Yesterday he had abundant stool.
He is agitated, preoccupied.
*Yesterday and the day before he took 1 teaspoonful but not today
because he is completely alright.*

Prescription
Sulphur 1 teaspoonful the 21st and 23rd and then nothing more.

[After a long gap in treatment there is a single entry.]

January 11th [1839]
When he swallows, his saliva stings in his throat.

Prescription
Inhale Nux vom. (one ounce?)

[Casebook **6**/380 (said to be continued from **IV**/355) contains several
entries, but only the first appears sequentially to belong here.]

May 23rd 1839
He has been working too hard.
*He has a feeling of oppression and weakness everywhere, as if neither
his chest nor his belly belong to him.*
A great deal of thirst and drowsiness.
Pain in the right side of the abdomen.
Today a weakness which is preventing him from swallowing.
His sleep is restless and agitated.
His skin is a little yellow.

Prescription
Sulphur 190c (. /190) diluted in 15 [tablespoonfuls of water and] 1 of
alcohol. Take 1 tablespoonful in one glass of water.

[Then resume reading the entries from **4**/355]

June 8th [1839]
*Nineteen days ago he had Sulphur 190c (. /190) diluted in 15
tablespoonfuls.*

He has had little colic-like pains. At the moment he only has little dull continuous pains, (cramping).
Always when the gripping pains take hold of him he is overcome by drowsiness and a sense of heaviness on account of the pain.
Appetite and sleep is good.
His morale is good. He has no fear.
The day before yesterday he took the last dose and then yesterday he was as he had been before the Sulphur 190c.

Repertory
(G) Yellowness of face: Hepar Sulph., Lyc., Nat. Mur.
(G) Compressing pain in lower abdomen.
(G) Drowsiness: Hepar Sulph., Lyc.

Prescription
Hepar Sulph 30c (. /X) in 15 [tablespoonfuls of water], 1 of alcohol, take 1 tablespoonful from one glass of the mixture and from it take 1 teaspoonful [daily].

June 15th [1839]
He has taken seven doses of Hepar Sulph. and is better. Has had one stool every day but with great difficulty.
His appetite and colour are a bit better.
He is walking about. His dreams are of fears, of hindrances; his breathing is difficult; he has nervous sensations in the pit of the stomach.
In the liver (and the ribs), a sense of pressure and fatigue.
He is less drowsy when the pains in the lower abdomen are not there.
He often has wind in the abdomen; he has a need for stool.

Prescription
Lycopodium 18c (. /VI) diluted in 15 [tablespoonfuls of water] and 2 [of alcohol]. Put 1 tablespoonful in a glass of water and take 1–2 teaspoonfuls from that daily.

June 28th [1839]
He took 2 teaspoonsfuls up until June 25th and then his eyes changed a little, he had dark circles round them. His colour is a little yellow.
When he began to take 1 teaspoonful his eyes got a little better.
On the 26th and 27th he took nothing during the day.

He has again suffered pain under the lower ribs on both right and left.
(This illness dates from 4 years ago).
Yesterday more drowsiness than today.
Good stool (soft).
He is sleeping and eating well.
Once more his breathing is a little restricted.

Prescription
Cinnabar 30c (. /X) 1 drop in 15 tablespoonfuls of water and 2 of alcohol. Take 1 tablespoonful from this and put into a glass, take 1–2 teaspoonfuls daily from this.

August 21st [1839]
For the last three or four days he has had a pain in the lower abdomen, heaviness with wind and desire for stool.
Because of this he has been tossing and turning, 20 times in the night.
The pain is on both sides, under both right and left ribs.
He has sensitivity in the lower ribs, especially when standing.
The pain in the liver went with the Cinnabar!!
Day time drowsiness. He is much weaker.
12 days ago he had diarrhoea badly for three or four days.
Good stool. Dreams of obstacles and escaping. (?Ign.)

Prescription
Hepar Sulph. 85c (. /85) in 7 tablespoonfuls [of water] and 1 [of alcohol]. Put 1 tablespoonful [from this in a glass of water and] take 1–2 teaspoonfuls daily.

Casebook entry: **4**/356

August 27th, [1839]
[A few days later they appear to get news from Musard who is now in London at an address in Leicester Square, presumably to conduct a concert.]
Since yesterday he has been short of breath, especially at night.
Sensation of swelling in the kidneys. When he is standing up he feels very tired, and worse.
Abdomen is sensitive to touch.
Always drowsy. He lies in bed apathetic and not wanting to move.
Always thirsty. A lot more wind in his belly, as if he had need to go and could not.

187

Always needs to move about.
Dreams of awkward situations.
Has a good appetite and stool.
Wants to be alone; is not cheerful.
Pain is full and heavy.
He should have Sepia.

Prescription
Sac lac in 4 [tablespoonfuls].
This morning he took another teaspoonful.

Casebook entry: **7**/67

August 31st [1839]
He had Hepar Sulph. 85c (. /85) on August 21st but since he continued to suffer greatly he had sac lac on the 27th in 4 [tablespoonfuls] and the pains have diminished since then.
This morning he has as much pain as yesterday (not strong) but less lassitude.
Stool every other day, a little, with difficulty.
He is not very breathless. The pain in the abdomen is still there: if it decreases then he has the tired or bruised pain.
Sleep agitated, restless. Better last night.
His skin is always dry. He is swollen after every meal. He always has pains in the side, both right and left, like wind pains (a kind of pressure).
Less drowsiness by day, waking up better.
He likes being in bed.
Drinking a lot.
Always wanting to stretch himself out.
Still a deceptive urging for stool.
Not much appetite.

Repertory
(G) Dry skin: Ars., Bell., Camph., Caust., Ph., Ac. Phos., Sil., Sulph., Cocc., Acon., Arn., Bism., Bry., Cham., Chin., Cocc., Puls.
Tough skin: Br., Camph., Cham., Cocc., Hyos., Ignat., Cocc., (Nux m.)

Prescription
Inhale Ignatia then sac lac for 4 days.

October 10th [1839]
He was very well until he returned to his apartment [in Paris] and then all the pains returned.
He has weakness in the stomach.
Breathing is difficult.
Scraping pain in the sides and the liver as well as the ordinary pains.
Pains like when he wants to go to stool and can't. Constant recurring pain.
In the morning he has pain in the sides when he breathes.
The pain in the liver is not constant: he can have that without having the other pains and can sometimes have the other pains without having the pain in the liver.
Stool good: he is no longer constipated.
At night the abdominal pains are better for lying on the belly.

Repertory
(F) Better for pressure: Alum., Ac. Mur., Iod., Kali., Mag. M.
(F) Weakness of the thighs and legs: Ac. Mur., Nat. Ph., Puls., Stann.

Prescription
Kali Carb 30c (. . /X) in 8 [tablespoonfuls of water and] 1 [of alcohol], put 1 tablespoonful in 1 glass of water and take 1–2 teaspoonfuls daily from that.

[No further entry apparently until]
August 25th 1840

[Casebook entry: **6**/380 continued from **IV**/355 (sic)]

Two months ago he had an attack of gout which lasted 6 weeks but all that remains of it now is a weakness in the right big toe.

Prescription
He is to plunge both feet in well water for a moment once or twice.
Hepar Sulph. 200c [Hepar Sulph. . /200/100]

Casebook entry: **4**/356 (bottom)

September 4th 1840
Skin rough on his left cheek.
A little burning in the big toe. Otherwise good.

189

Prescription
Plunge feet in water twice.
Hepar Sulph. 200c. [Hepar Sulph. 200/100 R. f...]

September 19th [1840]
No more roughness on his cheek.

Prescription
Hepar Sulph. 200c. (Hepar Sulph. 200/100)

September 23rd [1840]
The day before yesterday he had a little fever but yesterday afternoon his toe became swollen again after going out.
He has been putting his foot in cold water every day. His foot is heavy and the toe feels stiff when touched.

Prescription
Rhus Tox. 30c (. /X) in 2 glasses.
(November 21st in London. Sent him Rhus Tox. 24c (. /VIII)).

Casebook entry: **6**/380

January 14th 1841
(He had Rhus Tox. in England.)
In October 1840 he had another attack of gout which went away with the Rhus Tox. He also had a return of the abdominal pains: they were weak but resembled those of the bad illness.
Every time he felt the symptoms coming on he took Rhus Tox. and was relieved.
Four days ago he felt again the gouty pain in his right foot.

Prescription
Rhus Tox. 24c (. /VIII) in 15 [tablespoonfuls]. Put 1 tablespoonful in a glass and take 1 teaspoonful from it.

(He did not take the Rhus Tox. sent to London in November)

Casebook entry: **12**/23

March 30th 1841
From time to time there's a return of the old abdominal pains when the gout in the feet disappears. But the pains in the abdomen are much less strong.

Tension, tearing pains, (no breathlessness): but these pains are there only rarely.
If he sleeps on his belly on the floor he is better. He has a great feeling of weakness and of emptiness in the belly at these times.

Prescription
Sulphur LM 10 (10/oo), then sac lac in 4 [tablespoonfuls].

Casebook entry: **6**/380

April 3rd 1841 (in London)
On the 29th he complained that he had some pains in the abdomen for two or three days.
Yesterday he had a pain in the back just like when he has a strong desire for stool but cannot go.
General stiffness.
A feeling as if his abdomen was too full.
Breathless.

Repertory
(F) A feeling of terror, oppression. Br., Cupr., Tox.
(F) . . . navel: Ars., Bell., Carb. V., Ph.
(G) Occasional lancinating pains in liver: Calc., Caust., Lyc., Arn., Bry., Calad., Caps., Cocc., Ign., Ip., Puls. Spig.

Yesterday liquid stool without colic. Then strange pains.
He is not finding food bad.
Change of position improves things: he turns over a lot in bed.
The pain in the foot has completely disappeared.

Repertory
(F) Continuously thirsty: Br., Cupr., Sabad., Verat., Ars., Bell., Calc., Caust., Hepar Sulph., Nit Ac., Ac. Phos., Petr., Ph., Sil., Sulph.
Continuously drowsy.

Prescription
Inhale Lycopodium.
Then sac lac in 4 tablespoonfuls [of water decanted] from one glass of water to another and 1 teaspoonful from the second glass.

191

Casebook entry: **12**/23

April 9th [1841]
Looks better. Less diarrhoea.
After eating he has a lot of pulsating sensations in different places, but
less shuddering.
He still has the abdominal pains. Needs to stretch out.
Great fatigue on ascending. Less sleepiness in the day.
As soon as the abdominal pains cease his whole health returns.
No problem with the feet.

Repertory
(G) Sensation of an iron band under the hypochondrium.

Prescription
Inhale Lycopodium and take Lycopodium 30c (. /X) in 8 [tablespoons
of liquid and] ½ [of alcohol], take 1 teaspoonful [daily].

April 14th [1841]
Stools less liquid; the itching around the scrotum has gone but between
the prepuce and the gland he had some sweating and after that little
ulcers appeared with a stinging sensation.
The pulsations and shudderings passed.
Stiffness in all the limbs diminished.
The abdominal pain is almost gone.
The sleepiness in the daytime is almost gone.
(No chancre.)
The iron band sensation under the hypochondrium almost gone.
Less compulsion to stretch out.
Has a good appetite.

Prescription
Prepare what remains in 2 glasses and take 1–2 teaspoonfuls.

Casebook entry: **6**/380

April 23rd [1841]
On the tenth he had Sulphur. He has to walk about all the time –
keeping still is not good, whether he lies down or sits.
He's very constipated; sometimes has bruised pains in thighs and legs.
His belly is swollen as if he needed to go to stool but could not.

He has not been for three days.
Yesterday he had a bit of a gout-like pain in his hand and less thirst.
He is drowsy if he has no pains.
Insomnia at night.

Repertory
(G) Restless: Bell., Sep., Sil.

His genitals feel better; he has a good appetite.

Prescription
Belladonna, 4 doses of sac lac.

Casebook entry: **12**/23

April 27th [1841]

He had sac lac on the 23rd for four days and got better and better.
Still stiffness in the limbs.
He went 6 days without going to stool (yesterday an enema).
The abdominal pains at the front have passed but he has colicky pain (stinging) and his abdomen is painful to touch.
He is torpid. He is always drowsy. He is eating a little better, however.
He still has a little ulceration under the prepuce. His legs are tired.
He did not get up until the evening.

Prescription
Belladonna 30c in 8 [tablespoonfuls of water] and ½ [of alcohol] in 3 glasses. Take 1 teaspoonful from the last.

Casebook entry: **6**/380

May 10th [1841]

On the 6th the pain in his abdomen disappeared and he felt something in the third joint of his index finger.
On the 7th he felt a very painful pressure there for six hours during the night, with redness and swelling. His hand was very heavy with cramps and lancinating pains, as if the circulation had stopped.
Otherwise his health was good – the penis was less swollen.
Before the swelling the pain was worse and it diminished with the increase of the swelling.
At present when he moves (tense, tight pains in the joint) he feels a pain like an abscess in his bones.

A month ago he had three white pustules on the end of his penis.
Burning like fire.
At present he has dark red spots.
His thighs are more painful.

Casebook **6**/242

May 17th [1841]
He's very well. He's had no more abdominal pains. His hand is fine, even the finger joints. There's only a little swelling.
He is sleeping and eating well.
He's in excellent health.
When the right hand is exposed to the air it's more painful.

Prescription
Sulphur LM 10 (10/oo), dissolved in 7 [tablespoonfuls of water and]
1 [of alcohol], take 1 teaspoonful from it, then sac lac. (Sulphur 4/oo)

Casebook entry: **12**/24

May 29th [1841]
(Note written out of sequence in another book.)
Still has little colicky pains.
He has not had any Belladonna for four days: he was well and so he
stopped.
For the last three days he had more pain (decanting the medicine into
one glass) so he took it in two glasses for three days but the pains got
worse yesterday and the day before (especially in the night).
The soles of his feet hurt him.
Searing pain, exhausting pains.
The index finger of his right hand is very weak and when he bends it
there's painful stiffness. The toes are a little swollen.
Bowels are free.
Lancinating pains around the heart even in repose (old symptom).

Prescription
Sulphur LM 7 (7/oo) in 7 tablespoonfuls [of water] and $^1/_2$ [of alcohol]
in 3 glasses, take 1 teaspoonful from the 3rd.

Casebook entry: **6**/242

June 1st [1841]
(May 29th his right hand and the soles of his feet were painful again. I gave him Sulphur LM 7 in 7 [tablespoonfuls of water and] ½ [of alcohol], in 3 glasses.) [Adds this comment because the entry for May 29th is written in another book (**12**/24).]
On the first night, before taking the Sulphur LM 7 as soon as he had lain down in bed the pains took hold of him and did not calm down even slightly until 3 a.m. The pains were in both feet, especially the right.
On the 29th the pains continued; his feet were not very swollen; particularly in the soles and in the big toes there was not much inflammation or redness: very piercing lancinating pains.
Since yesterday evening he has not been able to get up.
He suffered a lot last night.
Yesterday he took a second teaspoonful. Today he hasn't taken one.
He thinks he has never had such severe pains. He cried out all night.

Prescription
Camphor 30c (. /X) in 8 [tablespoonfuls]. Take 1 teaspoonful every two hours.

June 4th [1841]
The pains calmed down with the Camphor at night. On the night of the 1st to 2nd they disappeared then on the 3rd they came back in the right hand where he had not suffered at all. The pains lessened substantially in the right foot but sometimes he has pain in the toes and the right hand, worse at night from midnight to morning.

Prescription
Rhus Tox. 30c (. /X) in 7 [tablespoonfuls of water and ½ of alcohol, decant] into 2 glasses and take 1 teaspoonful [daily from the second glass].

June 28th [1841]
Finished the Rhus Tox. 4–5 days ago. While he was taking it he felt no pain in either foot or belly. In the last three days the pain has come back in the big toe and a little in the abdomen.
Bowels free, good appetite, sleeping well.

Prescription
Hepar Sulph. LM 6 (6/o) in 8 [tablespoonfuls of water] and ¹⁄₂ [of alcohol] in 2 glasses. Take 1–3 teaspoonfuls [daily].

July 13th [1841]

He took herbal colchicum without consulting anyone other than himself (on the eighth, a single time) and suddenly the pain in the liver and intestines came back.
Very pale; pains in the hypochondrium. Cramping, heaviness in the lower abdomen and the groin.
Sensation of emptiness in the belly.
Constipation. On the twelfth he had an enema which produced a liquid stool.
He had a headache all night.
His belly is always swollen.
No appetite nor thirst ordinarily.
Yesterday in bed (he was in bed until today) he had several attacks of palpitations.
During the night he had to turn constantly onto his right side.

Prescription
Hepar Sulph. LM 5 (. /5/o) in 8 [tablespoonfuls of water] and ¹⁄₂ [of alcohol] decanted into 2 glasses. Take 1 teaspoonful [from the second glass daily].

July 17th [1841]

Abdomen perfectly well (*on the left and on the belly*).
Internal pains very good . . . passed . . .
A burning pain in the foot but only slight.
Good natural stools.
His big toe is painful again.
Some pains in the abdomen, heaviness and at the same time the sense of compression in the big toe like a vice.
(In England in September 1840 when he had an attack of gout he took 1 teaspoonful of Rhus Tox 24 (. /VIII) in 15 [tablespoonfuls of water] and ¹⁄₂ of alcohol for 15 days.)

August 4th [1841]

On the 28th in the evening he took a coffeespoonful. At 2 a.m. he had horrible gouty pains and took three more coffeespoonfuls: quarter of an hour later the pains had gone.

A good appetite. Finished yesterday.
Swelling of the feet has diminished.
His hands are cold and clammy.

Prescription
Hepar Sulph. LM 7 (7/o) in 15 [tablespoonfuls of water] and ½ [of alcohol], decant into 2 glasses and take 1–3 teaspoonfuls daily.

Casebook entry: **6**/243

August 16th [1841]
Since the 13th he has had a slight pain in the abdomen. Until the 13th he had been very well. The sensation of gout in the hands and feet had not increased. However, since the 13th it has increased a little in the left foot.
Otherwise he has a good appetite, is sleeping well and having a good stool.
His hands are no longer moist or cold.
He had no Hepar Sulph. on 14th, 15th, 16th.

Prescription
Sac lac in 7 [tablespoonfuls of water] and ½ [of alcohol], decanted into 2 glasses. Take 3 teaspoonfuls daily.

August 25th [1841]
Feet have been a bit painful since yesterday: until then he was perfectly well. Aching in the heel. Very little pain in the big toe. His hands are a little sensitive.

Repertory
(G) Pain in the foot: Rhus Tox.
(G) Pain in the big toe: Guai.

Prescription
Guaiacum 30c (. /X) in 7 [tablespoonfuls of water] and ½[of alcohol].
Take 1 teaspoonful daily [in a glass of water].

September 1st [1841]
Perfectly well in the joints, only a little pain. No depression.
Is sleeping, going to stool. No longer feels worse walking than resting.
No pain in the lower abdomen, no more tension in the thighs or shoulderblades, no swelling in the feet.

Prescription
Sac lac in 7 [tablespoonfuls of water] and ½[of alcohol].

September 6th [1841
Little gouty pains in the joints of fingers and feet have disappeared but the abdominal pains returned on the 4th. They are like the pains in the hypochondrium which prevent him from breathing.
Going to stool with more difficulty. He seems to have a much greater need to go.
Sleepy all the time.
Little appetite.

Repertory
(G) Contracting pain in feet: Rhus Tox., Dros., Nux .
(G) Contracting pain in the belly: Nit., Con., Magn., Sep., Sulph., Nat. Sulph., Zinc.

Prescription
Rhus Tox. 24c (. /VIII) in 7 [tablespoonfuls of water] and ½ [of alcohol] in 2 glasses. Take 1 teaspoonful [daily]. (Dros.)

September 18th [1841]
The abdominal pains stopped on the 3rd day after the third dose and after the sixth dose he felt gout in the joint of the right index finger; on the 13th he stopped taking the remedy and the gout went away.
At night he is as if he had cried and sobbed; he is angry and depressed and in the morning has abdominal pain and difficult stool.
Feet are completely well.
When he breathes his sides are painful from pressure and there is a sensation of swelling and fullness in the abdomen.
Less somnolence during the day.

Prescription
Hepar Sulph. LM 8 (8/o) in 15 [tablespoonfuls of water and] ½ [of alcohol]. 1 teaspoonful daily from 1 tablespoonful added to 2 glasses.

Casebook entry: **6**/293

October 8th 1841
Has still the pain in the belly and sometimes the lancinating pains in his feet. The bowels have loosened up.

Prescription
Ledum 30c (. /X) in 15 [tablespoonfuls of water and] ¹/₂ of alcohol in 2 glasses. Take 1 teaspoonful daily.

December 13th [1841]
Has been in London. Quin treated him and gave him Led., Hepar Sulph., Acon., Ipecac., Nux Vom., Cocc. and Coffea.

When he arrived in London he took Ledum. The preceding medicines given by Quin palliated the condition but did not put him into a good state. He has only got a little better in the last eight days under the influence of Coffea.
At present continuously breathless. Less so when he walks. More in the night. All his pains are aggravated at night.
The abdominal pains and those in the hypochondrium are less strong.
They are gripping, vice-like, windy pains in his bowels.
At present the pains are there when he is not constipated: in the past he has always been constipated when he has had the pains.

Repertory
(G) Better for movement: Puls., Rhus Tox., Samb.
(G) Worse for rest: Sil., Puls., Rhus Tox., Samb.

The pains begin afresh on almost the same day every week.
He's always cold, very chilly.

(G) Difficulty breathing: Nux Mosch.

Prescription
Inhale Nux Mosch., then Pulsatilla 30c (. X) in 8 [tablespoonfuls of water and] ¹/₂ [of alcohol]. 1 tablespoonful in a glass and take 1 teaspoonful from that daily.

December 15th [1841]
Difficulty in breathing diminished after inhaling Nux Mosch. but the pains are the same and he has not slept at all.

Sharp lancinating pains in the lower abdomen and in several parts of the body. Breathlessness diminished. Great pain in the epigastrium. Stiffness in the arms and legs. More pain at night.

Frequent desire to urinate; urine a little red. He believes he is getting more ill.

Prescription

Rhus Tox. 18c (. /VI) in 15 [tablespoonfuls]. 1 teaspoonful in a glass and take from that one teaspoonful, put it into a second glass and take from that 1 teaspoonful.

December 17th [1841]

The pains have decreased greatly. The soreness which he had in the liver (Dros) yesterday is no longer there. (NB Tox)

He has not yet had a single stool in six days despite having had two enemas.

He has not been able to sleep at night except a little from time to time.

After creamy soup or bouillon his urine is a little red.

Little thirst.

Pain in the arms and legs.

Morale much better.

Prescription

He is to take one teaspoonful from the third glass.

December 18th [1841]

At 11.30 he took one teaspoonful from the third glass and at 2.30 had a little attack: a little breathlessness which had passed by 4.00 p.m.

This morning the pains are much less but they still stop him from sleeping. This morning he was still restless but less so.

He feels the pains less today than yesterday.

Prescription

He is to take 1 teaspoonful daily from the third glass.

December 20th [1841]

On the 18th he took nothing and had a very abundant motion with great weakness.

He went to the ball. He came back at 3.30 with a huge appetite.

All day he wanted to eat frequently and the pains eased after each meal. After dinner he slept from 6–11 p.m. In the morning at 1 a.m. he took the Rhus Tox.

The night was good but he woke up wanting to eat as he had that morning.
He only has pains at intervals of 2–3 hours and even then they are slight.

Prescription
He is to take 1 teaspoonful in the morning.

Casebook entry: **10**/331

December 21st [1841]
He slept from 2–9.30.
He had only a little pain from time to time.
Very good appetite, good stool.

January 3rd 1841 (sic, but must be error for 1842)
Has taken nothing for fifteen days since the Rhus Tox. on December 15th.
On December 26th he felt slight pains in the night during the ball and on January 1st again, he had them as much before the ball but they went away during the ball.
On the 2nd he had a few pains after noon which continue and increase still.

January 19th [1842]
He's feeling well but has had a sore throat for three days.
Without swallowing he feels an internal swelling. He cannot breathe while swallowing, his throat feels as if it had a pin in it. (He has had this symptom several times in three months.)
A little shivering and fever in the night.
Previously very sweaty and with pains in the throat.
His mouth is full of saliva and he has gripping pains in his ears.
Less desire to drink.

Repertory
(G) Stinging without swallowing: Bell., Acon., Cham., Ign., Nat. Sulph., Puls., Rhus Tox., Spig.
(G) Inflammation in the mouth: Bell., Phos., Zinc.

It's 15 days since he finished the Tox.

Prescription
Inhale Belladonna LM 7 (7/o), then sac lac for 7 days.

Name: LAMBERT, Mme
Age 33, married

Casebook entries: **13**/43–5

The 33-year-old Mme Lambert was the daughter of another of Hahnemann's patients. She came for several months during 1841, complaining of pain and digestive problems: false hunger and constipation. She could only eat meat and potatoes.

Hahnemann began treatment with Sulphur in the LM potency but changed to Graphites in a high centesimal potency a week later, despite some improvement. The improvement continued but after another attack of indigestion she was given Antimonium Crudum 30c, followed by sac lac. After this, although she felt better in herself, she was still very constipated and so Plumbum and sac lac were given. The case then seemed to get a bit stuck. Although there had been an improvement in some respects and her digestion was certainly better, she was now getting lower abdominal pain, and diarrhoea from milk. At this point the prescription of Sulphur was resumed, in the LM 8 potency, and this was followed by a great general improvement which was maintained for over a month until a relapse was reported at the end of August. At around this time she appears to have been given Nux Vomica 192c (in between appointments?) followed by sac lac, whereupon there was a further improvement which lasted for a couple of months. Meanwhile the prescription of Sulphur LM was again renewed.

On November 1st she reported a great improvement in the abdominal symptoms but complained of sickness and headache when eating, whereupon she was given Kali Carb. to inhale and sac lac to take. These symptoms improved, but on her next visit the abdominal symptoms were again in evidence. Carbo Animalis was given, but a week later she was complaining of severe constipation and was given Ammonium Muriaticum. This seemed to do nothing, for when she came a week later she still had a lot of pain and Sulphur was resumed in a lower potency than before.

There is no further record of her visiting Hahnemann, so what happened is unclear. Her father also stopped visiting at this point, so there may have been some problem affecting the whole family.

May 22nd [1841]

(Menses are regular. Last period May 7.)
She has pain in the pit of her stomach and in the corresponding area of her back. Her stomach is hot and when her back hurts she has a dull pain, becoming piercing at times.
(She has had moxas of morphine on her epigastrium.)
She suffers from false hunger with gnawing sensations in the stomach.
She has been constipated for five or six days.
After eating she feels heavy and her hands burn.
Her digestion is extremely slow. She can only eat meat and potatoes.
She sleeps well but is woken by the pains in her stomach. She took purgatives and had diarrhoea for fifteen days.
She took the Waters of Sedlitz three days ago.
She feels better in the morning before lunch.

Prescription
Sulphur LM 7 (7/o) in 8 [tablespoonfuls of liquid]: put 1 [tablespoonful] in a glass of water and take 1 [teaspoonful from that daily].

May 28th [1841]

She no longer has pain in the stomach but she still feels the same weakness and fatigue.
Her urine is red.

Prescription
Graphites 192c (. /192) in 7 [tablespoonfuls]: put 1 [tablespoonful] in a glass of water and take 1 [teaspoonful from that daily].

June 5th [1841]

(Menses due 12th June)
She had indigestion after dinner for the first two days after taking the remedy. She had diarrhoea in the night with refluxes tasting of rotten eggs.
She looks better. She has more energy. She is no longer constipated and is having a bowel movement naturally.
She talks aloud in her sleep.

After dinner her face is red and her hands are hot.
She has eructations tasting of rotten eggs.

Prescription
Graphites 193 (. /193) in 7 tablespoonfuls.

June 15th [1841]
She had bad indigestion on June 5th, then her stool and her digestion improved.

Prescription
(Ant. Crud. 30c (. / X) in 7½ [tablespoonfuls of water] and ½ [of alcohol]: take 1 tablespoonful daily from 1 glass.)
  No 2: sac lac in 5 [tablespoonfuls of liquid]. From this put 1 teaspoonful into a glass of water, then a teaspoon from that into a second glass and from that take one teaspoonful [daily].

June 21st [1841]
She has less pain in her stomach but has heaviness every morning, a headache and sickness. Her eyes and face are hot.
She no longer has the fetid wind upward.
She is very constipated and hasn't had a stool for eight days. She had an enema yesterday.

Prescription
Sac lac in 7 [tablespoonfuls].

June 30th [1841]
Her stomach feels better. She has a little heaviness in the abdomen and headaches. She's very constipated.

Prescription
Plumbum 30c (. /X) in 7 [tablespoonfuls of water] and ½[of alcohol]: put 1 tablespoonful in a glass of water and take 1 teaspoonful [daily] from that.

July 3rd [1841]
(Menses due July 9th.)
She's well. She still had a feeling of heaviness in her abdomen the day before taking the Plumbum which she started on July 2nd. She has had

tasteless wind in her stomach (not upwards) and her mouth is watering. After the Plumbum she had sac lac.

Prescription
Continue sac lac.

July 16th [1841]
On the 11th she ate a little at lunchtime and upset her stomach greatly. It's better now; she has no more refluxes of rotten eggs and her digestion is better.
She gets a headache as soon as she has eaten dinner, with heaviness in her forehead. Her head feels dull and numb for about an hour, and her hands are cold – or dry and burning.
Since her stomach has improved she gets pains in the lower abdomen: there's a sensation of pressure with desire to urinate and a corresponding sensation in the kidneys.
For some time she has had diarrhoea when she drinks milk.
She's sad, feels like crying.
She no longer has any pains in her back.
Her urine is like water.
She is no longer weak and fatigued.
She no longer has refluxes tasting like rotten eggs.

Prescription
Sulphur LM 8 (8/o) in 7 [tablespoonfuls of water] and ¹/₂ [of alcohol]: put 1 [tablespoonful in a glass of water] and take 1 teaspoonful from that daily.

Casebook entry: **13**/44 (see facsimile, overleaf)

July 27th [1841]
Although she still has pains she is much better.

Prescription
Sulphur LM 9 (. /9/o) in 8 [tablespoonfuls].

August 6th [l841]
She's much better: she finished the prescription this morning.
She hasn't had a single pain in her stomach for six days.
She has had some pains in her womb.

Prescription
Sac lac.

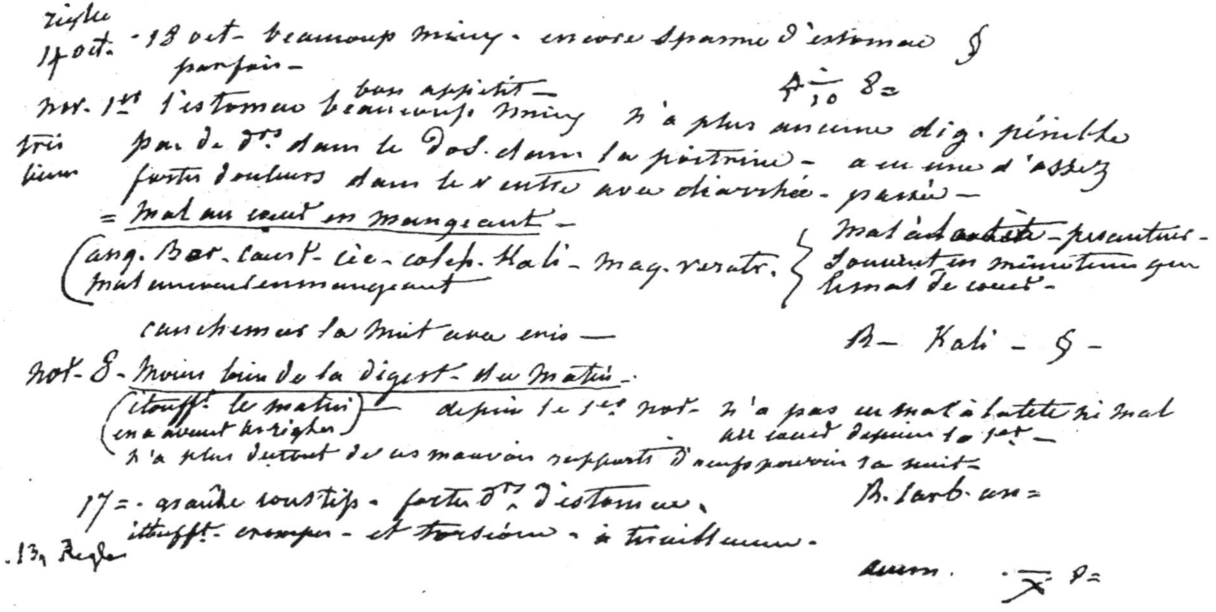
règle
14 oct. · 18 oct – beaucoup mieux · encore spasme d'estomac
parfois –
nov. 1er l'estomac beaucoup mieux bon appétit – n'a plus aucune dig. pénible
très bien pas de drs dans le dos. dans la poitrine – a eu une d'assez
fortes douleurs dans le ventre avec diarrhée – passée –
= mal au cœur en mangeant –
(ang. Bar. caust. cic. colch. Kali – mag. veratr.
mal au cœur en mangeant) } mal à la tête – presentimens – souvent ... mal de cœur –
cauchemars la nuit avec cris –   R – Kali –
nov. 8 – Moins bien de la digest. du matin –
(étouff. le matin / en avant hier) – depuis le 1er nov. n'a pas eu mal à la tête ni mal au cœur depuis le 1er –
n'a plus du tout de ces mauvais rapports d'oeufs pourris la nuit =
17 = · grande constip. · fortes drs d'estomac ·   R. Carb. ve =
étouff. crampes – et torsions · a tiraillemens –
. 13, Regle   Amm. · 8 =

Mme Lambert: This page was written by Melanie with Samuel adding the occasional note (viz. the last sentence in the August entry, and the rubric and '13 Regle' in the November 17th entry). Note here how Sulphur is prescribed in the LM potency, but interspersed with other remedies prescribed either in low centesimal potencies (Nux Vom., Amm.) or to be inhaled (Kali Carb., Carbo Veg.). It is difficult to be sure whether Mme Lambert was given Sulphur or Hepar Sulph. on August 20th.

August 20th [1841]
(Menses August 10th.)
She has been going to the toilet much more easily and has been eating soup for lunch. If she eats more she gets diarrhoea immediately. Digesting dinner still tires her a little but much less than it did.
On the eighteenth, after a long period of bleeding, she had a lot of pain in the womb.

Repertory
(G) Diarrhoea alternating with constipation: Ant. Iod., Tart., HS.

Prescription
Sulphur LM 10 (. /10/o) in 8 [tablespoonfuls].

August 30th [1841]
(Menses due September 12th.)
She has had indigestion several times. Liquids at lunch don't agree with her any more. She ate some meat and brought it back up. After several hours, when she thought she had digested the cutlet, she had suffocating sensations and pains in the back She has had pains in the lower abdomen with heaviness and heat in her kidneys.
Her stomach was better when the abdominal pains ceased.
(She has had Nux Vom. 192c (. /192).)

Prescription
Sac lac in 7 [tablespoonfuls].

September 14th [1841]
A great improvement in all the symptoms of the stomach and belly.
She is eating and digesting food better.
She looks better. She is plumper. She no longer has the heaviness in the body or the swelling in the abdomen.
While she was with us she had a sudden sharp pain in the right kidney.

Prescription
Nux Vom. Nux v. . / (potency omitted).

September 22nd [1841]
The kidney pains diminished but lasted until the following day.
She felt sick, tried to vomit.
She has suffered from nervous excitement.

Prescription
(Not noted)

October 18th [1841]
(Menses October 14th.)
Much better. Still has a spasm in her stomach sometimes.

Prescription
Sulphur LM 10 (. /10/o) in 8 [tablespoonfuls].

November 1st [1841]
(She's very well.)
Her stomach is much better. (Her appetite is good.) She no longer has any difficulty with digestion.
She has no pains in her back and chest. She had one episode of the quite strong abdominal pains with diarrhoea. It has passed.
Feels sick when she eats.

Repertory
(F) Feels sick on eating: Ang., Bar., Caust., Cic., Colch., Kali, Mag., Verat.
(She often has a headache and heaviness at the same time as the feeling of sickness.)
(She has nightmares with the attacks.)

Prescription
Inhale Kali Carb. and then take sac lac.

November 8th [1841]
Digestion not so good in the mornings.
(Sensation of oppression in the mornings before menses.)
She has had no headache or feeling of sickness since the remedy on November 1st.
(She has had no more reflux tasing of bad eggs in the night.)

Prescription
Inhale Carb. An.

November 17th [1841]
(Menses 13th.)
Great constipation; severe pains in the stomach. Sense of oppression, cramps, twisting and tearing pains.

Prescription
Amm. Mur. 30c (. /X) in 8 [tablespoonfuls].

Casebook entry: **13**/45

November 26th [1841]
Sense of oppression and pressing pains in the back. Heaviness in her belly and kidneys, no appetite for several days.
She has been feeling sick for several days and has not eaten.
She has a dry mouth, is very constipated.

Prescription
Sulphur LM 5 (. /5/o) in 7 [tablespoonfuls of water and] ½ [of alcohol].

Mme Lambert stopped coming at this point, as did her father.

Appendix II

The Manuscripts

Fifty-four volumes of Hahnemann's casebooks are preserved in the Institute for the History of Medicine in Stuttgart. Thirty-seven of these relate to Hahnemann's single-handed practice in Saxony from 1801–1835, seventeen to Hahnemann's joint practice with Melanie Hahnemann in Paris from 1835-1843. These seventeen volumes represent an original eighteen volumes, but the volumes now called 9a and 15 have been bound together and appear as one volume. Four of the volumes: 9a, 15, 16 and 17 relate to Melanie's solo practice, and the last three were written after Hahnemann's death. The table below indicates the period during which each of the seventeen Paris casebooks was used. The dates refer to the initial case-taking of the first and last cases recorded in the volume.

The Hahnemanns originally numbered their Paris volumes on the spine with Roman numerals in chronological order (I to XIV). However, these numbers have been eroded by time and are often missing. When the books were first added to the Stuttgart library, they were renumbered randomly and the pressmarks given to them did not relate to this original chronology. The original chronological sequence of the volumes has been established by the use of internal cross-reference, and the Institute has renumbered the volumes in accordance with the original chronology. I use this third sequence throughout. The chronological relationship between Volumes 3 and 4 remains a little uncertain. The table overleaf shows the relationship between the various sets of numbering. Volumes 9a and 15 (formerly Volumes 3a and 3b) are bound together.

The casebooks are of a reasonably uniform height and width (approx. 20cm x 16cm), but have a varying number of pages. They are bound in leather. Entries are usually made in brown ink, sometimes in a thick brown crayon-like pencil, sometimes in a lead pencil. The handwriting, though basically neat, is often hurried, cramped and difficult to read.

211

The Parisian Casebooks (Krankenjournale)

New IGM Number	Old IGM Number	Hahnemann Number	Dates of cases	Pages
2	12	II	7.12.1835–20.3.1836	ii+2–283
2a	1	petit vol.	17.3.1836–18.6.1837	iv+1–331+i
3	15	III	21.3.1836–6.8.1836	1–421
4	2	IV	12.8.1836–27.5.1837	ii+1–423
5	10	V	26.5.1837–7.10.1837	19–424
6	13	VI	6.10.1837–21.3.1838	ii+1–431
7	9	VII	24.3.1838–26.7.1838	ii+1–475
8	8	VIII	26.3.1838–3.9.1838	ii+1–462
9	11	IX	3.9.1838–4.12.1838	ii+1–467+4
9a	3a	MH	1.10.1838–2.8.1839	iv+1–168
10	6	X	19.10.1838–16.9.1839	iii+1–463
11	4	XI	4.1.1840–22.5.1840	1–477
12	14	XII	12.8.1840–9.5.1841	ii+1–562
13	7	XIII	9.5.1841–27.6.1842	1–470
14	5	XIV	5.10.1841–25.2.1844	ii+1–591
15	3b	MH	14.11.1845–12.7.1846	1–168
16	17	MH	13.1.1859–15.11.1860	1–479
17	16	MH	10.6.1863–19.10.1864	1–472

The records were kept up by both Samuel and Melanie. They were written almost entirely in French and therefore, at first, more in the hand of Melanie. Later, a pattern appears in which it looks as if Melanie normally took the case initially and did the bulk of the writing while Hahnemann listened. He then seems to have asked supplementary, clarificatory questions and to have written down the answers in his own hand.

From the very beginning there are marginal and interlinear notes in Hahnemann's hand and repertorisation is almost always written by him, at first taken from German repertories and later also from a French one. Sometimes almost the whole of the follow-up to a case is in Melanie's hand except the prescription; sometimes Melanie was responsible for recording the whole of an appointment; at other times it seems that Samuel was working by himself because Melanie's hand does not appear at all.

The original Volume I of the Paris series has been lost. Its existence, however, can be inferred from cross-references in later volumes. The remaining original volumes II-XIV survive and cover the dates indicated above.

In each volume, cases were entered sequentially according to the date on which the case was first taken. Any given case may have been continued for as long as there was some space in the volume. Characteristically a case was begun on a certain date: the initial details taken from the patient were entered in the book and several pages were left to allow for a record of follow-up appointments. Sometimes the amount of space left was insufficient for the number of follow-ups required, so the case had to be continued either elsewhere in the bound volume, in an unused space, or even in another bound volume. Sometimes the space left was more than was needed because the patient either got well quickly or did not come back. In these cases the space left over was either left blank or, more usually, filled with another case or a continuation of another case from elsewhere at a later date.

Because of this method of recording, it is not possible to say, for instance, that Volume 2 is a record of one year's practice and Volume 3 the record of another year. This would have been true for the German period of the practice, where Hahnemann's case records were kept in the form of a diary or day-book and all the cases of the patients who had appointments on particular days were recorded on the same page or sequence of pages. All that can be stated for the Paris volumes is that the cases recorded in the main text of Volume 2, for example, were first taken in the period December 1835 to mid-1836, and that there are prescriptions and fresh cases from various later dates inserted into spaces throughout the volumes. Likewise, the cases recorded in the main text of Volume 3 were first taken in the first half of 1836, and so on.

Volume 2, the first surviving volume of the series, covers an early period of the practice when initial histories were taken from December 7th, 1835 to March 20th, 1836. The book is densely packed with cases taken at this time, and with their continuations, which frequently extend to later years. It also includes continuations of cases originally recorded in the lost Volume I. Volume 2a was not included in the original numbering but was referred to as 'le petit volume'. It is a slimmer volume than the others and contains a number of cases taken by both Melanie and Samuel, although apparently by each working separately, since normally only one style of handwriting appears in most cases. Most of the cases are in fact written in Melanie's hand and a lot of the material is written in pencil or faint ink. It covers a period from March 1836 to June 1837. Volume 3 was used contemporaneously with this for a short time and covers the period from March to August 1836. This volume appears to have been the standard consulting-room volume. It is also crammed full with cases, continuations being entered on almost all blank pages. Volumes 4 to 6 continue to record in the same way consecutive cases first taken from August 1836 to March 1838.

At one particularly busy period of their practice during 1838 and 1839, the Hahnemanns kept up two books simultaneously, so that Volumes 7 and 8 are to some extent contemporaneous, both covering cases from March 1838 to later in that year (July and September 1838 respectively). Volumes 9 and 10 also share the same dates to some extent, beginning in September and October 1838 respectively and running in parallel for several months. Volume 10 is quite a scrappy collection and contains largely continuations of cases begun in other volumes. These four books are slightly less packed than some of the previous ones, presumably because there were two books kept up at the same time. At the same period Melanie also carried on her own individual practice and recorded the details in yet another book, Volume 9a. After this period the practice seems to have slackened off a little and Volumes 11 to 14 cover sequentially the period from the beginning of 1840 until Hahnemann's death and beyond, when the practice was continued by Melanie alone. Volume 11 covers a period from January to May 1840; the next volume in the sequence, Volume 12, does not begin until August 1840. There was no gap in the practice at this time, however – it was just that new cases were inserted into empty spaces in existing books during this period. Volume 13 takes over where the previous volume left off at the end of April 1841. Volume 14 follows on in its dates, taking the practice to the end of 1842. Subsequently, new cases were entered in spaces in this volume and Melanie continued to enter cases in this volume after Hahnemann died, so this volume contains the detail of her earliest completely independent practice. Volumes 15, 16 and 17 contain further sporadic material relating exclusively to Melanie's independent practice, though they by no means preserve a full record of it.

A serious difficulty in making a full analysis of the material stems from the fact that appointments are frequently not given a year date, only a month, so there is sometimes room for doubt about the year of entry, a doubt which can often but not always be resolved from context. Patients' names are always given, but their occupations and status only sometimes. Addresses and ages are usually but not always given. It is not always clear, in detail, what prescription has been made, as Hahnemann uses a system of abbreviations which is sometimes impenetrable. It is usually, however, possible to be clear about the actual remedy given, though not always about the potency and the actual method of administration.

Bibliography

Ackerknecht, E. H. *Medicine at the Paris Hospital, 1794–1848*, John Hopkins Press, Baltimore 1967.

Albrecht, F. *Christian Friedrich Samuel Hahnemann, ein biographisches Denkmal*, Leipzig 1851, published anonymously.

Albrecht, F. *Dr Samuel Hahnemanns Leben und Wirken. Ein Gedenkbuch auf Grund von Familienpapieren, . . . zweite vermehrte . . . neu bearbeitete Auflage*, Leipzig 1875.

Albrecht, F. *Treue Bilder aus dem Leben der verewigten Frau Hofrath Johanne Henriette Leopoldine Hahnemann*, Berlin 1865.

Allen, T. F., *The Encyclopedia of Pure Materia Medica*, (10 vols.) Boericke & Tafel, New York, Philadelphia 1874-9.

Ameke, W. *Die Entstehung und Bekämpfung der Homöopathie*, Berlin 1884, translated as *History of Homeopathy*, by A. E. Drysdale and ed. R. E. Dudgeon, E. Gould & Son, London 1885.

Archives de la médecine homoéopathique, publiées par une sociéte de médecins, ed. A. J. Jourdan, L. F. A. Simon et P. F. Curie, Paris 1834–7, 1838. See *Journal de la médecine homoéopathique.*

Barthel, P. 'Hahnemann's Legacy – the Q (LM) Potencies', in *British Homoeopathic Journal*, April 1991, Vol. 80, pp. 112–21, translated from 'Das Vermächtnis Hahnemanns – die fünfzigtausender Potenzen', *AHZ* 235: 47–61, 1990.

Baur, J. *Les manuscrits du Docteur Comte Sebastien Des Guidi*, (Vols. 1 and 2), Lyon 1985 and 1986.

Boenninghausen, C. M. F. Baron von, *Systematisch-alphabetisches Repertorium der antipsorischen Arzneien, nebst einem Vorworte des Herrn Hofraths Dr. S. Hahnemann über die Wiederholung der Gabe eines homöopathischen Heilmittels*, Münster 1832.

Boenninghausen, C. M. F. Baron von, *Systematisch-alphabetisches Repertorium der homöopathische Arzneien*, (2 vols.), Münster 1833 and 1835.(Vol. 1 is a 2nd edition of the first, 1832, repertory).

Boenninghausen, C. M. F. Baron von, *Versuch über die Verwandtschaften der homöopathischen Arzneien, nebst einer abgekürzten*

215

Uebersicht ihrer Eigenthümlichkeiten und Hauptwirkungen, Münster 1836.

Boenninghausen, C. M. F. Baron von, *Versuch einer homöopathischen Therapie der Wechselfieber*, Münster 1833, trans. and ed. P. P. Wells as *Intermittent Fever, together with the Repertory of C. von Boenninghausen*, Philadelphia 1837.

Boenninghausen, C. M. F. Baron von, ed. H. Dunsford, *The Pathogenetic Effects of Some of the Principal Homoeopathic Remedies, Compiled in Part from Boenninghausen's 'Versuch über die Verwandtschaften der hom. Arzneien' and 'Uebersicht der Hauptwirkungssphäre der antipsorischen Arzneien'*, London 1838.

Boenninghausen, C. M. F. Baron von, *Therapeutic Pocket Book*, Münster 1846.

Boenninghausen, C. M. F. Baron von, *Manual of Homoeopathic Therapeutics*, (trans. J. Laurie), H. Baillière, London 1847.

Boenninghausen, C. M. F. Baron von, *Quelques considérations sur la valeur caractéristique des symptômes*, Brussels 1860.

Boenninghausen, C. M. F. Baron von, *The Lesser Writings*, compiled by T. L. Bradford, (trans. L. H. Tafel), Philadelphia 1908.

Boenninghausen, C. M. F. Baron von, *Characteristics and Repertory*, ed. C. M. Boger, West Virginia 1905.

Boericke, W. and O., *Pocket Manual of Homoeopathic Materia Medica*, Boericke & Runyon, San Francisco 1927.

Bradford, T. L. *The Life and Letters of Dr Samuel Hahnemann*, Boericke & Tafel, Philadelphia 1895.

Bulletin de la Société Médicale Homéopathique de Paris, Paris 1845–7.

Campbell, A. *The Two Faces of Homoeopathy*, Norman & Hale, London 1984.

Chevalier, L. ed., *Le choléra, la première épidémie du XIXe siècle*, Bibliothèque de la Révolution de 1848, Vol. 20, La Roche-sur-Yon 1958.

Clarke, J. H. *A Dictionary of Practical Materia Medica*, (3 vols.) Homoeopathic Publishing Company, London 1925.

Cobban, A. B. C. *A History of Modern France*, (3 vols.), Jonathan Cape, London 1962–5.

Cook, T. *Samuel Hahnemann*, Thorsons, Northampton 1981.

Coulter, C. R. *Portraits of Homoeopathic Medicines*, North Atlantic Books, California, Vol. 1 1986, Vol. 2 1988.

Coulter, H. L. *The Divided Legacy: A History of the Schism in Medical*

Thought, (4 vols.), North Atlantic Books, California 1973, 1975, 1977, 1994.

Coulter, H. L. *Homeopathic Science and Modern Medicine*, (2nd edn), North Atlantic Books, California 1981.

Croll-Picard, A. S. *Hahnemann et l'homoéopathie*, Paris 1933.

Cullen, W. A. *Treatise of the Materia Medica*, (2 vols.), Charles Elliot, Edinburgh 1789.

De Courcy, G. I. C. *Paganini, the Genoese*, (2 vols.) University of Oklahoma Press 1957.

Delauney, M. *Pasteur et l'évolution des théories médicales*, Paris 1922.

Devrient, C. H. *The Homoeopathic Medical Doctrine or 'Organon of the Healing Art'*, (trans. from the 4th German edition), Samuel Stratten, Dublin 1833.

Dubos, R. and J. *The White Plague, Tuberculosis, Man and Society*, Gollancz, London 1953.

Dudgeon, R. E. (trans. and ed.), *The Lesser Writings of Samuel Hahnemann*, Headland, London 1852.

Dudgeon, R. E. *Organon of Medicine*, (trans. from 5th German edn), Headland, London 1849.

Dudgeon, R. E. *Materia Medica Pura*, (trans. from German), Homoeopathic Publishing Company, London 1880.

Dudgeon, R. E. *Lectures on The Theory and Practice of Homoeopathy*, Leath & Ross, London 1853.

Dudgeon, R. E. *Hahnemann's Therapeutic Hints*, collected and arranged by R. E. Dudgeon, E. Gould & Son, London 1894.

Durey, Michael, *The Return of the Plague: British Society and the Cholera 1831–32*, Ireland 1979.

Fisher, Peter, 'Research in Homoeopathy: A Selected Annotated Bibliography', *Journal of the American Institute of Homeopathy*, March 1987, Vol. 80, No 1, pp. 26–31.

Fritsche, H. *Samuel Hahnemann – Idee und Wirklichkeit der Homöopathie* (2nd edn), Stuttgart 1954.

Gibson, S. and R. *Homoeopathy for Everyone*, Penguin, London 1987.

Gregory, R. L. *The Oxford Companion to the Mind*, OUP, Oxford 1987.

Grove's Dictionary of Music and Musicians, (5th edn Erik Blom), Macmillan, London 1954.

Gumpert, M. *Hahnemann, die abenteuerlichen Schicksale eines älterlichen Rebellen und seiner Lehre der Homöopathie*, Berlin 1934.

Haehl, R. *Samuel Hahnemann, sein Leben und Schaffen*, (2 vols.), Leipzig 1922.

Haehl, R. *Samuel Hahnemann: His Life and Work*, trans. from the German by M. L. Wheeler and W. Grundy, ed., J. H. Clarke and F. J. Wheeler, (2 vols.), London 1931.

Hahnemann, M. *Notes confidentielles sur ma vie*, Paris 1847. In manuscript in IGM Stuttgart. See also Haehl 1931.

Hahnemann, M. *Letters to Samuel Hahnemann*, Köthen 1834–5. In manuscript in IGM.

Hahnemann, M. *Letters to Clemens von Boenninghausen*, Paris 1856. In manuscript in IGM.

Hahnemann, S. C. F. 'Versuch über ein neues Prinzip zur Auffindung der Heilkräfte der Arzneisubstanzen', in *Hufelands Journal*, Vol. 2, Nos. 2 and 3, 1796. Translated as 'Essay on a New Principle for Discovering the Curative Power of Drugs' in *Lesser Writings*, ed. R. E. Dudgeon.

Hahnemann, S. C. F. *Organon der rationellen Heilkunde* (1st edn), Dresden 1810.

Hahnemann, S. C. F. *Organon der Heilkunst*, (2nd edn), Dresden 1819.

Hahnemann, S. C. F. *Organon der Heilkunst*, (3rd edn), Dresden 1824.

Hahnemann, S. C. F. *Organon der Heilkunst*, (4th edn), Dresden and Leipzig 1829.

Hahnemann, S. C. F. *Organon der Heilkunst*, (5th edn), Dresden and Leipzig 1833.

Hahnemann, S. C. F. *Organon der Heilkunst*, (6th edn), ed. Richard Haehl, Leipzig 1921.

Hahnemann, S. C. F. *Organon der Heilkunst*, (6th edn), ed. K. Hochstetter, Chile, 1978.

Hahnemann, S. C. F. *Unterricht für Wundärzte über die venerischen Krankheiten*, Leipzig 1789. (Translated in *Lesser Writings*, ed. R. E. Dudgeon.)

Hahnemann, S. C. F. *Organon of the Rational Art of Healing*, (1st edn, trans. C. E. Wheeler), Everyman's Library, London 1913.

Hahnemann, S. C. F. *The Homoeopathic Medical Doctrine or 'Organon of the Healing Art'*, (4th edn, trans. C. H. Devrient), Samuel Stratten, Dublin 1833.

Hahnemann, S. C. F. *Organon of Medicine*, (5th edn, trans. R. E. Dudgeon), Headland, London 1849.

Hahnemann, S. C. F. *Organon of Medicine*, (6th edn, trans. J. Künzli et al.), Gollancz, London 1983.

Hahnemann, S. C. F. *Materia Medica Pura sive Doctrina de Medicamentorum* ... Dresden & Leipzig 1826-8. (*The Materia Medica Pura*, trans. and ed. G. Stapf and G. Gross, was originally published in German in 6 separate volumes: I: 1811, 1823, 1830; II: 1816, 1824, 1833; III: 1816, 1825; IV: 1818, 1825; V: 1819, 1826; VI: 1821, 1826).

Hahnemann, S. C. F. *Reine Arzneimittellehre* ... 3rd edn, Dresden and Leipzig 1830–3.

Hahnemann, S. C. F. *Materia Medica Pura*, (2 vols.) trans. and ed. R. E. Dudgeon, with annotations by Richard Hughes, Hahnemann Publishing Society, London 1880.

Hahnemann, S. C. F. *Die chronischen Krankheiten, ihre eigenthümliche Natur und homöopathische Heilung*, (1st edn), Dresden and Leipzig 1828.

Hahnemann, S. C. F. *Die chronischen Krankheiten, ihre eigenthümliche Natur und homöopathische Heilung*, (2nd expanded edn, 5 vols.), Dresden and Leipzig 1835–9.

Hahnemann, S. C. F. *The Chronic Diseases: Their Peculiar Nature and their Homeopathic Cure*, trans. from the second enlarged German edition of 1835 by L. H. Tafel, with annotations by Richard Hughes, Boericke & Tafel, Philadelphia 1896.

Hahnemann, S. C. F. *The Lesser Writings of Samuel Hahnemann*, coll. and trans. by R. E. Dudgeon, Headland, London 1852.

Hahnemann, S. C. F. *Sendschreiben uber die Heilung der Cholera*, Leipzig 1831. (Trans. R. E. Dudgeon, *Lesser Writings*.)

Hahnemann, S. C. F. 'The Medicine of Experience', in R. E. Dudgeon. ed., *The Lesser Works of Samuel Hahnemann*, London 1852.

Handley, R. *A Homeopathic Love Story*, North Atlantic Books, California 1990.

Hartlaub, C. G. and Trinks, C. F. *Reine Arzneimittellehre*, 3 vols., Leipzig 1828–31.

Hempel, C. J. *New Homoeopathic Pharmacopoeia and Posology*, (translation and expanded from Jahr's *Nouvelle pharmacopée* and the works of Büchner and Grüner with additions by Hempel), London 1850.

Hempel, C. J. *Jahr's New Manual of Homeopathic Medicine*, New York 1848–53. (translation of Jahr's Manual with extensive additions including a complete repertory).

Hempel, C. J. *Jahr's New Manual of Homeopathic Medicine*, New York 1848–53. (An expanded translation of Jahr's *Symptomen-Kodex*.)

219

Henne, H. (ed.) *Hahnemanns Krankenjournale*, Nos. 2 and 3, Haug, Stuttgart 1963.

Henne, H. 'Das Hahnemann-Archiv im Robert-Bosch-Krankenhaus in Stuttgart', *Sudhoffs Archiv*, Vol. 52, 1968.

Hering, C. *The Guiding Symptoms of our Materia Medica*, (10 vols.) Philadelphia 1879.

Hughes, R. *Manual of Pharmacodynamics*, (3rd edn), Leath & Ross, London 1876.

Hughes, R. *Manual of Therapeutics*, Leath & Ross, London 1877–8.

Hughes, R. *Cyclopaedia of Drug Pathogenesy*, Leath & Ross, London 1885.

Hughes, R. *The Principles and Practice of Homoeopathy*, Leath & Ross, London 1902.

Jahr, G. H. G. *Handbuch der Hauptanzeigen für die richtige Wahl der homöopathischen Heilmittel*, Düsseldorf 1834, ('Der mittlere Jahr').

Jahr, G. H. G. *Ausführlicher Symptomen-Kodex der homöopathischen Arzneimittellehre*, Düsseldorf 1835. (A much expanded version of the 1834 *Handbuch* above, published in Düsseldorf and Leipzig 1843-8. ('Der grosse Jahr'). Trans. Hempel.

Jahr, G. H. G. *Ausführlicher Symptomen-Kodex der homöopathischen Arzneimittellehre*, Düsseldorf 1835. (An expanded version of the 1834 *Handbuch* cited above.)

Jahr, G. H. G. *Ausführlicher Symptomen-Kodex der homöopathischen Arzneimittellehre*, Vol. 1, Düsseldorf 1843, Vol. 2, Leipzig 1848. (Known as 'Der grosse Jahr', this was an expanded version of the 1835 text, including Jahr's *Systematisch-alphabetisches Repertorium* (q.v.)). This was translated by Hempel in 1848, q.v.

Jahr, G. H. G. *Klinische Anweisungen zu homöopathischer Behandlung der Krankheiten*, Leipzig 1849. ('Der kleine Jahr').

Jahr, G. H. G. *General and Specific Therapeutics*, Paris 1857.

Jahr, G. H. G. *Du traitement du choléra*, Paris 1848.

Jahr, G. H. G. *Du traitement des digestions*, Paris 1859.

Jahr, G. H. G. *Nouveau manuel de médecine homoéopathique*, 2 vols., Paris 1840, 1841.

Jahr, G. H. G. *Ausführlicher Symptomen-Kodex der homöopathischen Arzneimittellehre*, 2 vols., Düsseldorf and Leipzig 1843–8, (Vol. 1, Dusseldorf 1843, Vol. 2, Leipzig 1848). See Hempel. This incorporates Jahr's *Systematisch alphabetisches Repertorium der homöopathischen Arzneimittellehre*, Leipzig 1848. (The complete work is a materia medica followed by a repertory giving all the remedies for eyes and then all the rubrics for eyes.)

Jahr, G. H. G. *Manual of Homoeopathic Medicine*, (trans. of 3rd. edn, J. Laurie), London 1841.

Jahr, G. H. G. *Nouvelle pharmacopée*, Paris 1841. See Hempel 1850.

Jahr, G. H. G. *Du traitement homoéopathique des affections nerveuses et des maladies mentales, Paris 1854.*

Jahr, G. H. G. *Venereal Diseases*, trans. C. J. Hempel, New York 1868.

Jahr, G. H. G. *Du traitement homoéopathique des maladies de la peau,* Paris 1850.

Jahr, G. H. G. *The Pathogenetic Effects of Homoeopathic Remedies*, Paris 1838 (trans. H. Dunsford).

Journal de la médecine homoéopathique, founded and edited by Léon Simon and Paul Curie. December 1833 to January 1835. It was absorbed by *Archives de la médecine homoéopathique,* (q.v.).

Journal de la médecine homoéopathique, publiée par La Société Hahnemannienne de Paris, Vols. 1–3, 1846–9. (This publication was subsequently fused with the *Bulletin de la Société Médicale Homoéopathique de Paris*, (q.v.) to form the *Journal de la Société Gallicane de Médecine Homoéopathique*, 1850–6 and 1857–9.

Kent, J. T. *Lectures on Homeopathic Philosophy,* Lancaster, Pa. 1900.

Kent, J. T. *Lectures on Homeopathic Materia Medica*, Philadelphia 1905.

Kishore, J. 'The Repertories in General', *The Homoeopath*, Vol. 6 (3 and 4), London 1987. This article was originally published as the introduction to the second edition of the *Kishore Cards*.

Kleinert, G. O. *Geschichte der Homöopathie*, Leipzig 1863.

Künzli, J. Naudé, A. and Pendleton, P. *Organon of Medicine by Samuel Hahnemann*, Tarcher, Los Angeles 1982.

Lafitte, P. J. *Symptomatologie homoéopathique, ou tableau synoptique de toute la matière médicale pure.* Vol. 1, Paris 1844.

Larnaudie, R. *La vie surhumaine de Samuel Hahnemann, fondateur de l'homoéopathie*, Paris 1935.

Legouvé, E. *Sixty Years of Recollections*, trans. Albert D. Vandam in 2 vols., Eden, Remington & Co., London 1893.

Lesch, J. E. *Science and Medicine in France: the Emergence of Experimental Physiology*, 1790–1855, Harvard University Press 1984.

Longmate, N. R. *King Cholera: the Biography of a Disease*, H. Hamilton, London 1966.

Miller, G. *The Adoption of Inoculation for Smallpox in England and France*, Pennsylvania 1957.

Mitchell, G. R. *Homoeopathy*, W. H. Allen, London 1975.

Nachtmann, Walter, 'Samuel Hahnemann als Arzt und Forscher. Wunschdenken und Wirklichkeit.' in *Jahrbuch des Instituts für Geschichte der Medizin der Robert Bosch Stiftung*, Vol. 5, 1986, pp. 65–86.

Nicholls, P. *Homoeopathy and the Medical Profession*, Croom Helm, London 1988.

Parish, H. J. and Cannon, D. A. *Antisera, Toxins, Vaccines and Tuberculins*, London 1962.

Parish, H. J. *A History of Immunization*, Livingstone, Edinburgh and London 1965.

Parr, B. *The London Medical Dictionary*, London 1809.

Quin, F. H. F. *Du traitement homoéopathique du choléra*, Paris 1832.

Quin, F. H. F. *Pharmacopeia Homoeopathica*, London 1834.

Ritter, H. *Samuel Hahnemann: sein Leben und Werk in neuer Sicht*, Heidelberg 1974.

Rowbottom, M. and Susskind, C. *Electricity and Medicine: History of their Interaction*, Macmillan, London 1984.

Sankaran, R. *The Spirit of Homoeopathy*, Bombay 1991.

Schmidt, Josef M., 'Die Materia Medica Samuel Hahnemanns', in *Jahrbuch des Instituts für Geschichte der Medizin der Robert Bosch Stiftung*, Vol. 6, 1987, pp. 111–27.

Schmidt, P. 'The Hidden Treasures of the Last Organon', in *British Homoeopathic Journal*, July 1954, pp. 134–56.

Schwanitz, H. J. *Homöopathie und Braunianismus 1795–1844: Medizin in Geschichte und Kultur*, Vol. 15, Stuttgart 1983.

Sheldrake, R. *The Presence of the Past: Morphic Resonance and the Habits of Nature*, Collins, London 1988.

Shorter, E. *A History of Women's Bodies*, Penguin, London 1982.

Showalter, E. *The Female Malady: Women, Madness, and English Culture, 1830–1980*, Virago, London 1987.

Stapf, J. *Archiv für die homöopathische Heilkunst,* ed. E. Stapf, 1822.

Tafel, L. H. (trans.) *The Chronic Diseases, Their Peculiar Nature and Homoeopathic Cure*, Philadelphia 1896.

Tischner, R. *Geschichte der Homöopathie*, in four parts, Leipzig 1932, 1934, 1937, 1939.

Treuherz, F. 'The Origins of Kent's Homoeopathy', *Journal of the American Institute of Homeopathy*, Vol. 77, No 4, December 1984, p. 130–49.

Tyler, M. *Homoeopathic Drug Pictures*, Homoeopathic Publishing Co., London 1942.

Ullman, D. *Discovering Homeopathy: Medicine for the 21st Century,* North Atlantic Books, Berkeley 1991.

Verbaime, E. *Un certain Hahnemann,* Paris 1962.

Vithoulkas, G. *The Science of Homeopathy,* New York 1980.

Waugh, R. (afterwards Hobhouse) *Life of C. S. Hahnemann,* C. W. Daniel, London 1933.

Weber, G. P. *Les hautes puissances de Jenichen,* Paris 1851.

Weber, G. P. *Codex des médicaments homoéopathiques ou pharmacopée pratique et raisonée,* Paris 1854.

Wheeler, C. E. *Organon of the Rational Art of Healing,* 1st edn trans., Everyman's Library, London 1913.

Wittern, R. 'The Robert Bosch Foundation and the Establishment of the Institute for the History of Medicine', *Clio Med.,* Dec 15, 1978 (1–2) pp. 89–91.

PATIENT INDEX
(Includes patients mentioned in textual commentary and notes)

GENERAL INDEX

Ackerknecht, E.H., 120
Aegidi, Dr, 28, 31
aggravation, 2, 34, 67, 68, 86, 91, 98, 116, 126, 131, 133, 134, 137, 141, 142, 148, 161, 163, 164, 168, 173, 199
Albrecht, F., 16
Allen, H.C., 36, 3, 62, 71
Allen, T.F., 88, 90
allopathic medicines (contemporary), 27, 30, 36, 38, 40, 60, 82, 86, 87, 94, 96, 101, 109, 110, 111, 149, 165
allopathic treatment, 39, 44, 66, 109, 112, 113, 114, 116, 117, 118, 119, 120, 164, 165
allopathy, 6, 7, 39, 40
alternation: *see* remedies, alternation of
Ameke, W., 16
amelioration, 29, 86, 95, 99, 101, 123
Analogy, Doctrine of, 88
Arles, Mr, 26, 29
arthritis and rheumatic complaints, 21, 25, 27, 45, 65, 79, 85, 95, 96, 97, 100, 127
attenuation, remedies of, 8, 133, 136, 138, 142, 143, 144, 146

Barvini, Mme, 27
Baur, J., 19, 32, 92, 108, 137
bleeding: *see* bloodletting
blisters, 112
bloodletting (venesection), 27, 95, 97, 107, 109, 111, 112, 113, 114, 119, 140, 148, 158, 208,
Boenninghausen, C.M.F. von, 12, 18, 19, 38, 62, 63, 65, 71, 74, 83, 88, 97
Boenninghausen, K., 12
Boericke, W., 19, 71, 86

Bolléaman, Dr, 28, 31
Bosch, Robert, 11, 13, 19, 88
bowel disturbances, 26, 35, 44, 79, 110, 171, 176, 183, 196, 198, 199, 203
Bradford, T.L., 16, 30, 108
Broussais, J.F., 27, 112, 113,
Brown, J., 91, 111, 212
Brunonism, 16, 111, 120
Bukhamian, Dr, 28, 31

Campbell, A.C.H., 75
Candegabe, E.F., 72
Cannon, D.A., 63
casenotes, 11, 12, 13, 14, 15, 16, 23, 24, 25, 29, 30, 32, 40, 65, 66, 70, 74, 82, 83, 86, 97, 98, 102, 109, 116, 126
catarrhal conditions, 25, 38, 85, 92, 96
cauterisation, 94, 100, 112, 113
chagrin, 44, 72, 78; *see also* grief
chancre, syphilitic, 25, 26, 40, 93, 94, 96, 97, 192
Chapelin, Dr, 119
cholera, 26, 33, 34, 39, 40, 44, 60, 61, 63, 85, 110
Chronic Diseases, 11, 36, 61, 81, 90, 118, 120, 125, 131, 135, 136, 137
Clarke, J.H., 92, 97, 108
constitution, 25, 37, 39, 62, 70, 71, 72
consumption: *see* phthisis
convulsive states, 33, 45, 46, 79, 80, 83, 90, 91, 94, 119, 138, 139
Cook, T.M., 16
Coulter, C.R., 88
Coulter, H.L., 36, 118
Croll-Picard, A.S., 16
Croserio, C., 10, 22, 26, 29
Cruncher, Dr, 32
Cullen, W.A., 5, 17, 111

REMEDY INDEX
(Excludes remedies cited in rubrics)

232

Classical Homoeopathy, Dr Margery Blackie, 1986, reprinted 1990 with Repertory. The complete teaching legacy of one of the most important homoeopaths of our time.   0906584140

Comparative Materia Medica, Dr E. F. Candegabe, 1997. Detailed comparative study of thirty-seven remedies by one of the Argentinian masters.   0906584361

Everyday Homoeopathy (2nd Edition), Dr David Gemmell, 1997. A practical handbook for using homoeopathy in the context of one's own personal and family health care, using readily available remedies.
0906584442

Homoeopathic Prescribing, Dr Noel Pratt, revised 1985. A compact reference book covering 161 common complaints and disorders, with guidance on the choice of the appropriate remedy.   0906584035

Homoeopathic Treatment of Beef and Dairy Cattle, The, C. E. I. Day, MRCVS, 1995. Describes how homoeopathy may be used in the care of cattle, both as individuals and in a group.   090658437X

Homoeopathic Treatment of Eczema, Robin Logan, FSHom (in preparation). A textbook on the homoeopathic treatment of this condition.   0906584477

Homoeopathy, Dr T. P. Paschero (in preparation). Dr Paschero's major work on the subject.   0906584418

Homoeopathy as Art and Science, Dr Elizabeth Wright Hubbard, 1990. The selected writings of one of the foremost modern homoeopaths.   0906584264

Homoeopathy in Practice, Dr Douglas Borland, 1982, reprinted 1988 with Symptom Index. Detailed guidance on the observation of symptoms and the choice of remedies.   090658406X

In Search of the Later Hahnemann, Rima Handley, DPhil, FSHom, 1997. A study of Hahnemann's practice in Paris, with material from his casebooks of that period.   0906584353

Insights into Homoeopathy, Dr Frank Bodman, 1990. Homoeopathic approaches to common problems in general medicine and psychiatry.
0906584280

Introduction to Homoeopathic Medicine (2nd Edition), Dr Hamish Boyd, 1989. A formal introductory text, written in categories that are familiar to the medical practitioner.   0906584213

The Beaconsfield Homoeopathic Library

Materia Medica of New Homoeopathic Remedies, Dr O. A. Julian, paperback edition 1984. Full clinical coverage of 106 new homoeopathic remedies, for use in conjunction with the classical materia medicas.   0906584116

Mental Symptoms in Homoeopathy, Dr Luis Detinis, 1994. A comparative study of the Mind rubrics in Kent's *Repertory*.   0906584345

Studies of Homoeopathic Remedies, Dr Douglas Gibson, 1987. Detailed clinical studies of 100 major remedies. Well-known for the uniquely wide range of insights brought to bear on each remedy.
0906584175

Tutorials on Homoeopathy, Dr Donald Foubister, 1989. Detailed studies on a wide range of conditions and remedies.   0906584256

Typology in Homoeopathy, Dr Léon Vannier, 1992. A study of human types, based on the gods of Antiquity, and the remedies which are relevant to them.   0906584302